Controlled Nuclear Chain Reaction

The First 50 Years

Controlled Nuclear Chain Reaction

The First 50 Years

Published with support from

The University of Chicago
Board of Governors
for Argonne National Laboratory

American Nuclear Society
La Grange Park, Illinois USA

Library of Congress Cataloging-in-Publication Data

Controlled nuclear chain reaction : the first 50 years.
    p. cm.
  ISBN 0-89448-557-1
    1. Controlled fusion—Research—History. 2. Nuclear
energy—Research—History. 3. Nuclear reactors—Research—
History. I. American Nuclear Society.
QC791.745.C66   1992
621.48'4—dc20   92-34150
                                        CIP

ISBN: 0-89448-557-1
Library of Congress Catalog Card Number: 92–34150
ANS Order Number: 690032

Copyright © American Nuclear Society
555 North Kensington Avenue
La Grange Park, Illinois 60525 USA

Typography: Kate Weisel
Printed in the United States of America

CONTENTS

FOREWORD

This year we mark the 50th anniversary of the first controlled nuclear chain reaction, CP-1, achieved by the group led by Enrico Fermi at the University of Chicago on December 2, 1942. This first chain reaction was one of the key events of the Manhattan Project. In addition to its wartime implication, it also signaled the birth of the peaceful applications of nuclear energy.

On the occasion of this 50th anniversary, it is appropriate to consider the history of the peaceful applications of nuclear energy. It is a complex history that has been truly global, involving many technologies and applications across many national programs. In addition to technical and economic issues, the history has been enmeshed in political and social issues including the ever present one of public and institutional acceptance. The issues have also often been entwined in the public mind with military considerations.

This book has been prepared in conjunction with the American Nuclear Society/European Nuclear Society meeting commemorating CP-1. It is clear that no small volume, such as this one, can touch on more than a small fraction of this complex history. But it is the hope of the authors that the book will convey some of the history and give some indication of the many beneficial impacts that have resulted from the peaceful applications of nuclear energy.

The book has been prepared by volunteer effort of a large number of people over several months. Much use has been made of already available material with appropriate permission and attribution. But the authors take responsibility for choice of material and for the balance or lack of balance on the many possible issues to be covered. Every effort has been made to assure the accuracy of the facts presented.

It is the belief of the authors that the beneficial impacts of nuclear energy, while already enormous, represent only a small fraction of the benefits yet to be gained and that this brief history of the first 50 years of the controlled nuclear chain reaction represents only the first phase of the nuclear era.

INTRODUCTION

Few of us knew anything about the event of December 2, 1942, at the time. I actually do recall the article in *Popular Science* about powering huge ships with tiny amounts of something called uranium. I remember the atomic bombs and the end of the war, and then we began to see news articles in magazines, and even items in the Movietone News in the theaters on Saturday afternoons. There were reports about research that could open new frontiers, books about the scientists who were engaged in this work, and news stories about wonderful ways to generate unlimited amounts of electricity.

I remember thinking, "What would it have been like to have been one of those scientists at Stagg Field? What a challenge it would be to make this new and promising source of energy really work!" Many engineers and scientists decided to focus their careers on developing nuclear power, understanding radiation, and making these new technologies serve mankind.

Over the years, the dream of finding an unlimited source of energy has been replaced by hard reality. We have participated in five decades of hard work, some well-earned successes, and some disappointments as well. Through it all, scientists and engineers believed that having enough affordable energy can improve the standard of living, can make life more meaningful and satisfying, can make the environment cleaner and healthier, and can help societies earn the wherewithal to make life better for the future. Nuclear power makes an important contribution to the world's energy supply: one-fifth of the world's electric power.

We have been told that we must examine our technology in relation to human values. We are challenged to test both our basic beliefs about the need for energy, and also the risks and benefits of using nuclear fission to produce electric power.

There is ample evidence around the globe that the benefits of energy used wisely more than exceed the risks and environmental impacts. When one looks at nations and regions in which energy is scarce and terribly expensive, it is brutally clear that environmental damage is greater, health care is poorer, life spans are shorter, and both the quality of life today and hope for the future are sadly lacking.

And since the time of the first experiments of 50 years ago, nuclear scientists and engineers have respected the risks of our technology. Safety has been paramount, a remarkable record of safety has actually been achieved, and the goal has always been the containment of radiation and ultimate safe disposal of radioactive wastes.

None have made the claim that nuclear power is the only answer—that it should, or even could, do it all. Diversity is a cardinal principle of electric power supply planning. However, fossil fuels will most likely continue to supply the bulk of the world's energy through the next century. The nuclear community actively supports the development of alternative energy sources and fully agrees with the need for a massive commitment to energy conservation and improved efficiency.

Many thoughtful people believe that even with unprecedented successes in conservation and alternative energy sources, many new electric power plants will be essential. And if mankind is serious about the environment in cities and about global emissions to the atmosphere, the majority of these will have to be nuclear. A number of nations, with developing as well as industrialized economies, are moving ahead resolutely. In the United States, it is our task not only to be ready, but also to explain effectively why nuclear power needs to be in the energy marketplace. This, without doubt, should be our contribution to the legacy of the Nuclear Pioneers.

A. David Rossin
President, American Nuclear Society
September 1992

ACKNOWLEDGMENTS

Robert Avery, General Chairman of the 1992 American Nuclear Society/European Nuclear Society Meeting commemorating the 50th anniversary of the CP-1 experiment, conceived the idea for a commemorative publication and provided the inspiration for the project. Harold McFarlane, charged with overall leadership of the project, was responsible for much of the final writing and editing. David Rose developed the original outline, pulled together the story of CP-1, and helped with final editing of the manuscript. Michael Lineberry refined the concept, wrote the chapter on the future of nuclear applications, and provided tough editorial review throughout.

A large cadre of volunteers, mostly current or retired employees of Argonne National Laboratory, was enlisted to help with the project. Roger Tilbrook took on the task of telling the illustrated story of the development of nuclear power outside the United States and provided general editorial assistance. Michael Goff, in charge of collecting photographs and obtaining permission to use them, also rooted out numerous errors in the manuscript. Joseph Braun helped organize the first draft, tracked down photographs, and designed the cover with the help of ANS graphic artist Kathryn O'Brien. William Hannum, Howard Kittel, David Lennox, and Jacques Reifman each organized and drafted a chapter. Those who did research, drafted material, and helped locate suitable photographs included: Paul Bacca, Samit Bhattacharyya, Igor Bodnar, Leslie Burris, Peter Collins, Charles Dickerman, Stephen Herring (EG&G, Idaho), Richard Lindsay, Kwang Park, Charles Rice (Rice, Inc.), Bob Seidel, Richard Smith, George Vandergrift, and Douglas Warinner. Also providing valuable help with reference material or photographs were: Vincent Aquino, Ira Bornstein, Harry Bryant, John Carpenter, Ira Charak, Julia Czarny, Edwin Hahn, George Imel, Alton Klickman, Judy Krieger, Vladimir Minkov, Jill Morgenthaler, Daniel Pruett, Maxine Rosenkrance, Joe Ross, Alfred Schneider (MIT), Cynthia Wilkinson, and James Chimbidis.

Argonne National Laboratory, the American Nuclear Society, the University of Chicago, the U. S. Council for Energy Awareness, and the U.S. Department of Energy generously provided photographs and reference material to help make this project possible. Many people around the United States provided timely help with photographs: Jon Payne and the staff of *Nuclear News;* Anthony Draper and Richard Meyers at USCEA; Dave Moran at DOE; Dana Spiardi and Kathy Horvat at Westinghouse; Celeste Volker at SteriGenics; Doug Fouquet at General Atomics; Charles Bagnal and Bob Hartranft at ABB Combustion Engineering; L. R. Wallis and Ann Kilty at GE; Marilyn Druby and Sandi Murdock at Westinghouse Hanford Company; Steven Wyatt at DOE–Oak Ridge; Michael Pollack at Rockwell International; Lyle LaFaver at Pacific Gas and Electric; John Metzger at Baltimore Gas and Electric; Mary Wells at GPU Nuclear; Gary Wald at Commonwealth Edison; Ray Golden at Florida Power and Light; Donna King and Michael Lumpe at The Cleveland Electric Illuminating Company; Victoria Edwards at Tass/Sovfoto; Lt. Commander March of the U.S. Navy; Don Andrews at Arizona Public Service; Mandy Comai and W. J. McGee at Yankee Atomic; Frank Creane at Boston Edison Company; Michael Wood at Philadelphia Electric; Albert Ritardi at AGNS; Sanford Rock at Allied Signal; Glen Walker at Houston Lighting and Power; and James Steets at New York Power.

The illustrated history of nuclear power development outside the United States was only possible with the help of people in several countries and organizations: Atomic Energy of Canada Limited—Susann Camus, Stan Hatcher (retired), Ian Hastings, John Macpherson, Tammy Ohta; Ontario Hydro—Alan Holt, Sylvia Kovesfalvi; Electricité de France International—Audra Dainora, Henry Herbin; Ambassade de France Aux Etats-Unis—Bertrand de Galassus, Christiane Houzet; AEA Technology—Lorna Arnold, Maureen Dale, Margaret Gowing, Bridget Jefferies, Peter Wright; British Nuclear Fuels plc—Jake Kelly; Joint European Torus—John Maple and Carol Simmons; Cogema—Amour Kouakou; NNC Limited—John Penny; Nuclear Electric—June Hassett, Nick Mullane, Robin Thornton; Power Reactor and Nuclear Fuel Development Corporation—A. Kuboyama; Tokyo Electric Power—Takashi Karasaki; Ex-Soviet Nuclear Society—Andrei Gagarinski, Sergei Kryukov; and *Nuclear Engineering International*—Janet Wood. Jacques Bouchard of the Commissariat à l'Energie Atomique and J. I. Bramman of AEA Technology provided summaries on the future direction of European nuclear programs.

Lorretta Palagi and Mary Beth Gardner of the ANS Publications Department provided essential guidance and encouragement for the project.

Cover photographs provided courtesy of: Chicago Historical Society—Gary Sheahan's painting of the CP-1 experiment; NASA and GE Astro Space Division—Apollo astronaut deploying SNAP-27 RTG nuclear power source; Commonwealth Edison Company—Zion Nuclear Power Station; and GE Medical Systems—nuclear medical imaging.

Controlled Nuclear Chain Reaction

The First 50 Years

CP-1 scientists at the University of Chicago on December 2, 1946, the fourth anniversary of their success. *Back row, left to right:* Norman Hilberry, Samuel Allison, Thomas Brill, Robert G. Nobles, Warren Nyer, and Marvin Wilkening. *Middle row:* Harold Agnew, William Sturm, Harold Lichtenberger, Leona Woods Marshall, and Leo Szilard. *Front row:* Enrico Fermi, Walter H. Zinn, Albert Wattenberg, and Herbert L. Anderson. (Courtesy of Argonne National Laboratory)

ONE

Chicago Pile No. 1: The First Controlled Nuclear Chain Reaction[1]

"The Italian navigator has landed in the New World," said Compton.

"How were the natives?" asked Conant.

"Very friendly."

This cryptic telephone message between Arthur Compton, director of the Chicago Metallurgical Project, and James B. Conant at Harvard University marked the first announcement of the successful completion of the epochal experiment under the Stagg Field Stadium at the University of Chicago on December 2, 1942. It was considerably later, near the close of World War II, before the world at large learned that this date marked the birth of the nuclear age.

Stagg Field, the site of CP-1. (Courtesy of Argonne National Laboratory)

[1]This chapter is drawn extensively from "The First Reactor, 40th Anniversary," DOE/NE-0046, U.S. Department of Energy (Dec. 1982).

December 2, 1942

Herbert L. Anderson, one of Enrico Fermi's principal collaborators on the Chicago Pile experiment, captures the excitement of those assembled in his account of the event[2]:

> As it happened, on December 2, a group from DuPont arrived in Chicago, as part of a review they were conducting, to see where they could do the most good among the various activities of the Manhattan District. When they arrived, Compton told them that Fermi was about to carry out his test of the first chain reaction. There were quite a few people already there. It was getting kind of crowded. There were the people who put it together and there were others who wanted to be present and had enough clout

| Enrico Fermi led the CP-1 team. (Courtesy of Argonne National Laboratory) | Herbert L. Anderson worked with Fermi on CP-1 and earlier at Columbia. (Courtesy of Argonne National Laboratory) |

> to get in. The DuPont group was invited to select one of their number to witness the performance. They chose Crawford Greenewalt. It was quite a show!
>
> Fermi was in charge. He soon began to issue instructions to George Weil who was down on the floor where he could manipulate one of the cadmium control rods. To

[2]H. L. Anderson, "The First Chain Reaction," in *The Nuclear Chain Reaction—Forty Years Later: Proceedings of a University of Chicago Commemorative Symposium*, The University of Chicago (1984).

register the neutron intensity, we had a boron-trifluoride counter. It was connected to a scaler which operated a mechanical counter. The counter made a loud sound every time it registered a count. It went clack! And after the next 16 pulses from the boron-trifluoride counter, it would go clack again. Just by listening you could tell what the neutron intensity was.

When he began all the control rods were in the pile. Fermi ordered all removed except the one operated by George Weil. He then asked George to pull that rod out a foot. Fermi recorded the activity as indicated by the counter, so many clacks per minute. The rod was pulled out another foot and a new measurement was made. Fermi would put each measurement on a graph and then, with a little slide rule, he would calculate where the next point ought to go. He had done his homework and knew what to expect. Each data point was analyzed on the spot.

These preliminary measurements went on for a while and in due course it became lunch time. It was Fermi's habit to go to lunch at noon and this occasion was no exception. It wasn't a good idea to do an important experiment on an empty stomach.

The serious work began after lunch. Fermi calculated that the system would become critical by removing eight feet of the cadmium strip. He called for the strip to be pulled one foot at a time. The increase in intensity was obvious to everyone on the balcony. You could hear those clacks and each time the strip was removed further the clacks came faster and faster. At each step Fermi would record the result, make a calculation, and announce something like "The next time we pull out the strip by one foot, the rate will go from 600 to 1200 a minute." Then the rod would be pulled out and everybody could tell by the sound that the prediction was in the right ball park. They weren't exactly on but each time he got closer. You got the feeling that Fermi really knew what he was doing, that he had everything under control.

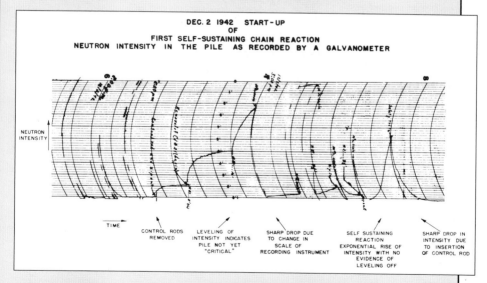

Chart recording of the neutron intensity in CP-1 during the first self-sustaining chain reaction. (Courtesy of Argonne National Laboratory)

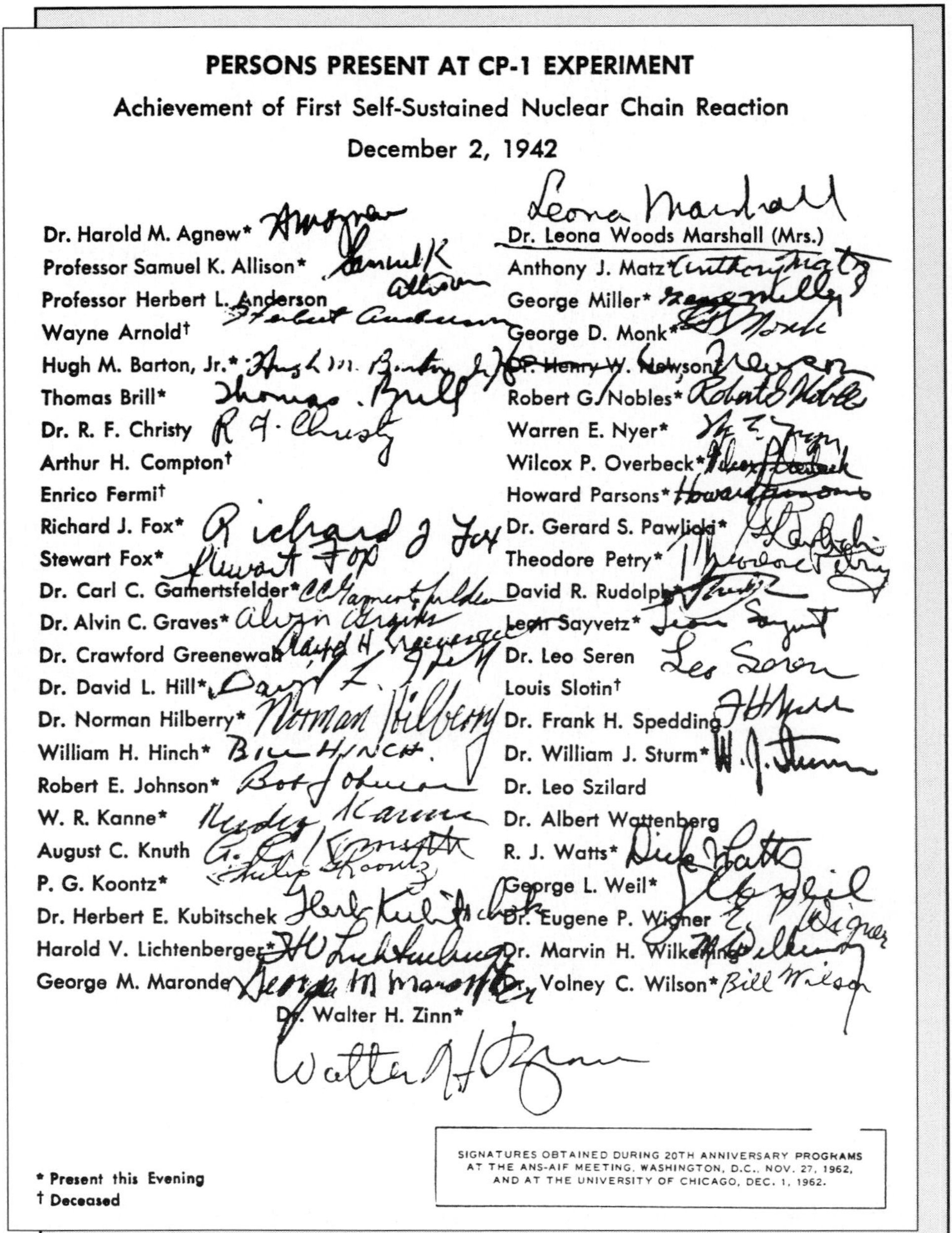

PERSONS PRESENT AT CP-1 EXPERIMENT

Achievement of First Self-Sustained Nuclear Chain Reaction

December 2, 1942

Dr. Harold M. Agnew*
Professor Samuel K. Allison*
Professor Herbert L. Anderson
Wayne Arnold†
Hugh M. Barton, Jr.*
Thomas Brill*
Dr. R. F. Christy
Arthur H. Compton†
Enrico Fermi†
Richard J. Fox*
Stewart Fox*
Dr. Carl C. Gamertsfelder*
Dr. Alvin C. Graves*
Dr. Crawford Greenewalt
Dr. David L. Hill*
Dr. Norman Hilberry*
William H. Hinch*
Robert E. Johnson*
W. R. Kanne*
August C. Knuth
P. G. Koontz*
Dr. Herbert E. Kubitschek
Harold V. Lichtenberger*
George M. Maronde

Dr. Leona Woods Marshall (Mrs.)
Anthony J. Matz*
George Miller*
George D. Monk*
Dr. Henry W. Newson*
Robert G. Nobles*
Warren E. Nyer*
Wilcox P. Overbeck*
Howard Parsons*
Dr. Gerard S. Pawlicki*
Theodore Petry*
David R. Rudolph*
Leon Sayvetz*
Dr. Leo Seren
Louis Slotin†
Dr. Frank H. Spedding
Dr. William J. Sturm*
Dr. Leo Szilard
Dr. Albert Wattenberg
R. J. Watts*
George L. Weil*
Dr. Eugene P. Wigner
Dr. Marvin H. Wilkening
Dr. Volney C. Wilson*

Dr. Walter H. Zinn*

SIGNATURES OBTAINED DURING 20TH ANNIVERSARY PROGRAMS AT THE ANS-AIF MEETING, WASHINGTON, D.C., NOV. 27, 1962, AND AT THE UNIVERSITY OF CHICAGO, DEC. 1, 1962.

* Present this Evening
† Deceased

Signature sheet of those present at CP-1. The sheet was prepared at the twentieth anniversary celebration of CP-1. (Courtesy of Argonne National Laboratory)

At a certain point he announced that by pulling out the cadmium strip a final foot and one-half, the pile would go critical. Instead of leveling off as had been the case before, the intensity would continue to rise indefinitely in an exponential fashion.

The rod was pulled out the specified amount and you could hear the counters clicking away—clickety-clack, clackity-click. They went faster and faster and then at a certain point there was silence. The rate had become too great for the counters to follow. It was a dramatic moment. An important threshold had been passed. Attention turned to the chart recorder. It

Walter H. Zinn worked with Fermi on CP-1 and earlier at Columbia. (Courtesy of Argonne National Laboratory)

was silent but could record much higher levels of intensity. You watched a pen moving across the scale as the chart advanced. It produced the well-known record which has since become famous.

The intensity kept rising and soon the pen was off-scale. So the scale was changed, the pen returned to a point near zero and then began to move across the scale again. The rise in intensity was exponential as the record shows. After a change in scale by a factor of 10, it was understandable that some of the onlookers might become a little nervous. They didn't hear anything, they didn't feel anything, but they knew that a dangerous activity was mounting rapidly. Everyone's eyes were on Fermi. It was up to him to call a halt. But he was very confident and calm. He wanted the intensity to rise high enough to remove all possible doubt that the pile was critical. He kept it going until it seemed too much to bear. "Zip in," he called, and Zinn released his rope. The control rod he held went in with a bang and the intensity dropped abruptly to comfortable levels.

Everyone sighed with relief. Then there was a small cheer. The experiment was a success.

The Chicago Pile No.1 experiment was intended to demonstrate that a self-sustaining, controllable nuclear chain reaction could be achieved. Four years before the December 2 experiment, the discovery was made that when an atom of uranium was bombarded by neutrons, the uranium atom sometimes split, or *fissioned*. Later it had been found that when an atom of uranium fissioned, additional neutrons were emitted and became available for further reaction with other uranium atoms. These facts implied the possibility of a chain reaction. The facts further indicated that if a sufficient quantity of uranium could be brought together under the proper conditions, a self-sustaining chain reaction would result.

Enrico Fermi, a refugee from Fascist Italy, the Canadian-born Walter Zinn, and their associates at Columbia University had been working to determine possible designs for a uranium chain reactor. Among other things, they had to find a suitable moderating material to slow the neutrons from the relatively high emission velocities they had at the time of fission. In July 1941, experiments with uranium were started to obtain measurements of the so-called "reproduction factor," called "k_∞," which was the key to

Leo Szilard, who had patented a chain reaction process in 1934.
(Courtesy of Argonne National Laboratory)

the problem of a chain reaction. If the number of neutrons produced in a system for each neutron absorbed in the uranium nucleus could be made sufficiently greater than one, a chain reaction would be made to take place in a mass of material of practical dimensions. If it were less than one, a self-sustaining chain reaction could not occur no matter how large the reactor.

One of the first things that had to be determined was how best to arrange the uranium and moderator in the reactor. Fermi and the Hungarian-born Leo Szilard suggested placing the uranium in a matrix of the moderating material, thereby forming a cubical lattice of uranium. This placement appeared to offer the best opportunity for a neutron to encounter a uranium atom. Of all materials possessing the proper moderating qualities, graphite was the only one which could be obtained in sufficient

Arthur H. Compton directed the Chicago Metallurgical Project, 1942–1945. (Courtesy of Argonne National Laboratory)

quantity with the desired degree of purity. Impurities were an important consideration, for while pure graphite readily scatters neutrons, absorption reactions are rare. Neutron absorption in commercially available graphite is strongly influenced by the presence of such naturally occurring impurities as boron and vanadium. Neutrons parasitically absorbed by any nucleus other than uranium would reduce the fraction of neutrons available to continue the chain reaction.

The study of graphite-uranium lattice piles was begun at Columbia in July 1941. In December 1941, after reorganization of the uranium project, Arthur H. Compton was placed in charge of this phase of the work, under the Office of Scientific Research and Development, and it was decided that the chain reactor program should be concentrated at the University of Chicago. Consequently, early in 1942 the Columbia and Princeton groups were transferred to Chicago where the Metallurgical Laboratory was established.

At Chicago, the work on graphite-uranium piles was extended to increasingly larger sizes. As size increases, the fraction of neutrons leaking from the pile decreases. Just as with parasitic absorption, any neutrons that leak from

A typical block of CP-1 graphite, with uranium pellets. (Courtesy of Argonne National Laboratory)

the pile are lost to the chain reaction. It was known that with naturally occurring uranium, at best little margin existed for leakage and absorption if a self-sustaining chain reaction, i.e., a critical reactor, were to be possible. The pile would have to be large to minimize leakage, and it would need to have a minimum of impurities in either the graphite or the uranium to minimize parasitic absorption.

By July 1942, the measurements obtained from these experimental piles had gone far enough to permit a choice of design for a test pile of critical size. At that time, the dies for pressing uranium oxide were ordered to be made from Zinn's design. This was a crucial step, since the entire construction of the pile depended on the shape and size of the uranium pieces.

Uranium oxide had to be used because metallic uranium of the desired purity did not exist. Although several manufacturers were attempting to produce the uranium metal, it was not until November that any appreciable amount became available. By mid-November, Westinghouse Electric and Manufacturing Company, Metal Hydrides Company, and F. H. Spedding, who was working at Iowa State College at Ames, Iowa, had delivered several tons of the highly purified metal, which was placed in the pile as close to the

Drawing depicting CP-1. (Courtesy of Argonne National Laboratory)

center as possible. Scientists and engineers undertook whatever tasks needed to be done, no matter how foreign from their usual endeavors. Thus, Canadian-born Norman Hilberry handled the procurement program for moderating material and uranium oxides, and Richard L. Doan headed the procurement program for pure uranium metal.

Although the dies for pressing uranium oxide were designed in July, additional measurements were necessary to obtain information about controlling the reaction, to refine estimates of the final critical size of the pile, and to develop other data. In all, 30 experimental piles of less than critical size were constructed before the final pile was completed.

Construction of the main pile in the squash court under the West Stands of Stagg Field was begun on November 15. It was named Chicago Pile No. 1 (CP-1). In essence, a small

> # Construction of the main pile in the squash court under the West Stands of Stagg Field was begun on November 15.

factory was set up to machine the graphite to the right size, with holes drilled for the uranium. Fermi wanted to build the pile with the shape as close to spherical as possible. This would minimize the surface-to-volume ratio and, consequently, the leakage of neutrons. Fermi could then make the best use of the material that would become available. The project gained momentum with machining of the graphite blocks, pressing of the uranium pellets, and the design of instruments. Fermi's two "construction" crews, one under Zinn and

CP-1 during construction, showing the pattern of graphite blocks and uranium pellets.
(Courtesy of Argonne National Laboratory)

the other under Anderson, worked almost around the clock. The instrument work was led by V. C. Wilson.

To avoid absorption of neutrons by the nitrogen in the air, the pile was enclosed in a balloon cloth bag, manufactured by Goodyear Tire and Rubber Company. The air in the bag could be evacuated and replaced with carbon dioxide, which would absorb fewer neutrons. This capability was put in as a contingency, should such action become necessary to achieve criticality after the pile had reached maximum size.

The bag was hung with one side left open. In the center of the floor a circular layer of graphite bricks was placed. This and each succeeding layer of the pile was braced by a wooden frame. Alternate layers contained the uranium. This layer-on-layer construction allowed a roughly spherical pile of uranium and graphite to be formed.

Before the structure was half complete, measurements indicated that the critical size at which the pile would become self-sustaining was somewhat less than had been anticipated in the design. Day after day the pile grew toward its final shape. As the size of the pile increased, so did the nervous tension of those working on it. Scientifically they knew this pile would be self-sustaining; all the measurements indicated that it would. But still the demonstration needed to be carried out. As that eagerly awaited event drew closer, the scientists gave increasing attention to details, the accuracy of measurements, and the exactness of their construction work.

Fermi guided the pile construction and design every step of the way. So exact were his calculations, based on measurements taken from the partially finished pile, that days before its completion and demonstration on December 2, he was able to predict almost to the exact brick at which point the reactor would become self-sustaining.

During the afternoon of December 1, tests indicated the critical size was rapidly being approached. At 4:00 P.M. when the last layer of graphite and uranium bricks was placed on the pile, Zinn and Anderson made several measurements of the activity within the pile. They were certain that when the control rods were withdrawn, the pile would become self-sustaining. Both had agreed, however, that should measurements indicate the reaction would become self-sustaining upon control rod withdrawal, they would not start the pile operating until Fermi and the rest of the group could be present. Consequently, the control rods were locked and further work postponed until the following day.

About 8:30 on the morning of Wednesday, December 2, the group began to assemble in the squash court. At the north end of the squash court there was a balcony where Fermi, Zinn, Anderson, and Compton were grouped around the instruments. The remainder of the observers crowded the little balcony.

After the lunch break, Fermi reassembled his team at 2:00 P.M. Weil stood ready at the control rod. As the experiment continued, Wilcox Overbeck could

Photograph of the painting by Gary Sheahan depicting the events at CP-1. (Courtesy of Chicago Historical Society)

George Weil handled the final control rods for CP-1. (Courtesy of Argonne National Laboratory)

Eugene Wigner. (Courtesy of Oak Ridge National Laboratory)

Leona Woods Marshall was a member of the CP-1 team. (Courtesy of Argonne National Laboratory)

be heard calling out the neutron count over an annunciator system. Leona Woods Marshall, Anderson, and William Sturm were recording the readings from the instruments. Suddenly, Fermi smiled and announced, "The reaction is self-sustaining." The group watched for 28 minutes while the world's first nuclear chain reactor operated. Then, Fermi called, "OK, Zip in," to Zinn who controlled that rod. The time was 3:53 P.M. It was all over.

Right after Fermi ordered the reaction stopped, the Hungarian-born Eugene Wigner presented Fermi with a bottle of Chianti wine. Fermi uncorked the bottle and served it in paper cups so all could drink. Silently, without toasts, they drank to success—and to the hope that they were the first to succeed.

Events Leading to CP-1

Years of international scientific effort and study lay behind this demonstration of the first self-sustaining nuclear chain reaction. The evolution of scientific information leading up to CP-1 might be viewed in two principal periods: the more recent period dates back to the work of German scientists Otto Hahn and

Eugene Wigner's famous Chianti bottle. (Courtesy of Argonne National Laboratory)

Fritz Strassman in 1938; the earlier period dates back to the work of the English physicist, Ernest Rutherford, in 1902.

Forty years before CP-1 a discipline of nuclear science did not even exist as such. It was in 1902, six years after the discovery of natural radioactivity, that Rutherford concluded that the energy of the radioactive emanations, when compared to the energy released in ordinary chemical reactions among atoms and molecules, was larger by a factor of a million. He pointed out that this energy must be stored in the atoms that are the source of the radioactivity. In 1911, Rutherford reported on the first of his famous experiments on alpha-ray scattering by atoms. The results of these experiments led to the development of the nuclear model of the atom, with its positively charged massive nucleus surrounded by a compensating cloud of negatively charged electrons carrying only a tiny fraction of the atomic mass.

The advent of the nuclear atom made possible the quantized model of the hydrogen atom developed by Neils Bohr. Subsequently, in 1919, Rutherford showed that it was possible to transform one element into another, to "transmute" elements of small atomic weight into other elements, by bombarding them with an alpha particle, i.e., the nucleus of a helium atom.

In 1932, James Chadwick of England discovered the neutron, an electrically neutral nuclear particle having the same mass as the proton. Because of its electric neutrality, even the slowest moving neutron can penetrate into the depths of an atom and enter its nucleus. The scientific significance of this possibility was immediately recognized—neutrons of any energy are absorbed into nuclei, thereby transmuting them from one species to another, a process that has become a primary source of artificial radioactivity.

A select few realized the possible technological significance of the existence of the neutron. Until the neutron was discovered, the only known nuclear reactions required enormous energy, or high temperatures like those in the sun or stars, to initiate them because of electrical repulsion between nuclei. The neutron might make it possible to release the energy stored in the nuclei. To obtain useful power, it was necessary to identify a reaction capable of releasing a significant amount of energy and to sustain a high, but controlled, rate of such reactions.

> Because of its electric neutrality, even the slowest moving neutron can penetrate into the depths of an atom and enter its nucleus.

If 1932 was the year of the neutron, 1933 was the year of artificial radioactivity, a discovery of Irène and Frédéric Joliot-Curie. Their demonstration that properly aimed particles could change ordinary atoms of one element into another was a signal to the world of physics that the elements were no longer

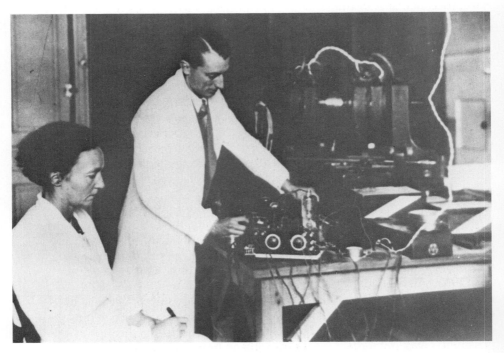

Irène and Frédéric Joliot-Curie, the discoverers of artificial radioactivity. (Courtesy of Electricité de France)

to be considered immutable, and radioactivity no longer a property confined by nature to radium and a few other less active elements. The notion of alchemy was no longer merely a fantasy.

In the meantime the scientific possibilities of the neutron were being aggressively exploited by Fermi. In 1934, he rapidly demonstrated that nearly every element in the periodic table might undergo a nuclear transformation when bombarded by neutrons. His most important target element was uranium, the heaviest element then known, the bombardment of which produced results not explainable by the physics of the day. Fermi concluded that he had probably found new radioactive elements still heavier than uranium, i.e., "transuranic."

The period from 1934 to 1939 was marked by the studies of the apparent transuranic elements, but the results seemed to raise more questions than they answered. In 1938, Hahn and Strassmann, working at the Kaiser Wilhelm Institute in Berlin, unambiguously identified one of the radioactive species as an isotope of the relatively light element, barium. Upon submitting their work to the German scientific journal *Die Naturwissenschaften*, Hahn wrote to his former partner, Lise Meitner, who was now an emigrant in Stockholm. Lise Meitner was very much interested in this phenomenon and immediately attempted to analyze the results of the experiment mathematically. She reasoned that the barium and the other residual elements were the result of a fission, or breaking, of the uranium atom. But when she added the atomic masses of the residual elements she found this total was less than the atomic mass of the uranium.

There was but one explanation: In fissioning, or splitting, the uranium forms two elements of approximately half its original mass, but not exactly half, and some of the mass of the uranium "disappears." Meitner and her nephew Otto Frisch who, having fled Nazi-controlled Germany, was working with Niels Bohr in Copenhagen, suggested that the mass that disappeared was converted into energy. According to Albert Einstein's theory, advanced in 1905, the relationship between mass and energy was given by the equation $E = mc^2$ (energy is equal to mass times the square of the speed of light). With this relationship, the energy release would be of the order of 200,000,000 electron-volts for each atom undergoing fission. The reaction that would release a large amount of energy had been found.

> The reaction that would release a large amount of energy had been found. Nearly 30 years before the discovery of fission, Einstein himself had said his theory might be proved by further study of radioactive elements.

Nearly 30 years before the discovery of fission, Einstein himself had said his theory might be proved by further study of radioactive elements. Bohr had been planning a trip to America to discuss various problems with Einstein who had found a haven at Princeton's Institute for Advanced Studies. But when Bohr came to America, the principal item he discussed with Einstein was the report of Meitner and Frisch. Bohr arrived at Princeton on January 16, 1939. He talked to Einstein, Wigner, and his former student, J. A. Wheeler. From Princeton the news spread by word of mouth to neighboring physicists, including Fermi at Columbia, where he too had found a place of refuge. Fermi and his associates immediately began to work to find the heavy pulse of ionization that could be expected from the fission and the consequential release of energy.

While these experiments were under way, Fermi attended a conference on theoretical physics at George Washington University in Washington, D.C., where he discussed the problem of fission with Bohr. Fermi mentioned the possibility that neutrons might be emitted in the process. If so, the emitted neutrons might be the key to obtaining a high rate of reactions. During their

On December 2, 1942, man achieved the first self-sustaining controlled nuclear chain reaction in Chicago Pile Number 1 (CP-1) at The University of Chicago. This lithograph of the event is printed with ink made from graphite used in CP-1.

Leo Szilard   Arthur H. Compton   Enrico Fermi   Eugene P. Wigner

Photograph of a lithograph, produced with graphite from CP-1, commemorating the events at CP-1. (Courtesy of Argonne National Laboratory)

conversation, their ideas of the possibility about a chain reaction began to crystallize.

Years earlier Leo Szilard had conceived of the possibility of releasing energy by making use of what physicists call $(n,2n)$ reactions, in which one neutron enters a nucleus and two neutrons emerge. He reasoned that under the right conditions such a "chain reaction" could produce significant amounts of heat from the energy released by the reaction. In fact, in 1934 Szilard patented such a process on the assumption that beryllium could be used as the active material that would undergo the $(n,2n)$ reaction. It proved to be impossible, but Szilard's concept was very similar to the process later exploited in the fission chain reactor.

Within a month after the conference, experimental confirmation of Meitner and Frisch's deduction was obtained from four laboratories in the United States: Carnegie Institution of Washington, Columbia University, Johns Hopkins University, and the University of California at Berkeley. Later it was learned that similar confirmatory experiments had been carried out by Frisch and

Meitner on January 15. Frédéric Joliot-Curie in France also confirmed the results and published them in the January 30 issue of the French scientific journal, *Comptes Rendus.*

On February 27, 1939, Zinn and Szilard began their experiments at Columbia to find the number of neutrons emitted by the fissioning uranium. At the same time, Fermi and his associates, Anderson and H. B. Hanstein, began their investigation of the same problem. The results of these experiments were published side by side in the April issue of the American Physical Society journal, *Physical Review,* and showed that a chain reaction might be possible since the uranium emitted additional neutrons when it fissioned.

BIBLIOGRAPHY

Anderson, H. L. 1984. "The First Chain Reaction," in *The Nuclear Chain Reaction— Forty Years Later: Proceedings of a University of Chicago Commemorative Symposium.* The University of Chicago.

Anderson, H. L., E. Fermi, and H. B. Hanstein. 1939. "Production of Neutrons in Uranium Bombarded by Neutrons," *Phys. Rev.* **55.**

Anderson, H. L., E. T. Booth, J. R. Dunning, E. Fermi, E. N. Glasoe, and F. G. Slack. 1939. "The Fission of Uranium," *Phys. Rev.* **55.**

———. 1982. "The First Reactor, 40th Anniversary," DOE/NE-0046. U.S. Department of Energy.

Hahn, Otto, and F. Strassman. January 1939. "Uber den Nachweis und das Verhalten der bei der Bestrahlung des Uransmittels Neutronen Entstehenden Erdalkalzmetalle," *Die Naturwissenschaften* **27.**

Hewlitt, Richard G., and Oscar E. Anderson, Jr. 1989. "Historical Perspectives: Dawn of the Nuclear Age, Reminiscences of Pioneers in Nuclear Fission," in *Remarks from a Symposium of the 1982 Winter Meeting of the American Nuclear Society.* American Nuclear Society, La Grange Park, IL.

Hewlitt, Richard G., and Oscar E. Anderson, Jr. 1962. *The New World 1939/1946: Volume 1: A History of the United States Atomic Energy Commission.* The Pennsylvania State University Press.

Lapp, Ralph E. 1953. *The New Force: The Story of Atoms and People.* Harper and Brothers, New York.

Szilard, Leo, and Walter H. Zinn. 1939. "Instantaneous Emissions of Fast Neutrons in Interaction of Slow Neutrons with Uranium," *Phys. Rev.* **55.**

Turner, Louis A. 1940. "Nuclear Fission," *Rev. Modern Phys.* **12.**

Chalkboard at EBR-I commemorating the first use of atomic energy to produce electricity. (Courtesy of Argonne National Laboratory)

TWO

Development of Nuclear Power Plants in the United States

Following World War II, the United States had all the resources necessary to begin development of nuclear electric power plants. The Manhattan Project had pulled together many of the finest scientific minds of Western Europe and North America. Young American scientists and engineers had the opportunity to train under these nuclear pioneers, honing skills that would be invaluable in developing peaceful applications of the controlled nuclear chain reaction. Much of the technology developed in making the atomic bomb was adaptable to developing nuclear reactors for the production of electrical power; the United States was the only country that had full access to that technology.

Besides the large plutonium production reactors that had been built as a part of the Manhattan Project, low-power research reactors existed as well as a uranium-enrichment capability.

U.S. Atomic Energy Commission Established

The U.S. Congress placed the development of nuclear energy under civilian control with passage of the Atomic Energy Act of 1946 (also known as the McMahon Act). This legislation ensured the continued military development of nuclear energy, but primarily established the initial framework for private industrial involvement in the

> Young American scientists and engineers had the opportunity to train under these nuclear pioneers, honing skills that would be invaluable in developing peaceful applications of the controlled nuclear chain reaction.

development of peaceful applications. The federal government retained the sole right to own fissile materials and the plants that produced them. The act established the U.S. Atomic Energy Commission (AEC), whose charter was to administer and regulate all production and use of atomic power. President Harry Truman appointed David Lilienthal as the first chairman of the initial five-member governing board of the AEC. Among the major programs of the newly formed AEC were production of fissionable materials; research in fields such as biology, radiation effects, and metallurgy; and production of thermal and electrical energy from the atom.

From Concept to Commercial Viability

Soon after its inception the AEC canceled or suspended existing work on power reactor development. The AEC commissioners realized that developing an economical nuclear power plant would be a challenging project, despite its scientific feasibility being assured. The AEC's long-range plan called for starting with a program of research and testing. The first major step was taken in 1948 when the construction of several research and test facilities was authorized. The new facilities included a high-flux materials testing reactor (MTR), an experimental fast breeder reactor (EBR-I), and a prototype pressurized water reactor (S1W, initially known as STR or Submarine Thermal Reactor) for submarine propulsion. These facilities were located at a new site in Idaho called the National Reactor Testing Station, which today is known as the Idaho National Engineering Laboratory (INEL). Within the AEC, a Division of Reactor Development was formed to direct the emerging nuclear power effort.

The path to nuclear power development was wide open in the United States. Other countries, forced to begin development with natural uranium, confronted the same constraints that Fermi and his CP-1 team had faced—either a graphite or heavy-water moderator had to be used. But because of its uranium-enrichment capability, the United States was free

The Materials Test Reactor, MTR. (Courtesy of US Department of Energy)

First nuclear electricity provided by EBR-I on December 20, 1951. (Courtesy of Argonne National Laboratory)

to consider any combination of fuel type, moderators, coolants, and steam cycles. This gave rise to a seemingly endless variety of reactor concepts, many of which were actually tested.

Nine years after the end of the CP-1 experiment, electricity was generated for the first time from heat produced in a nuclear reactor. Only one building was illuminated by the EBR-I experiment that December day, but to some extent the event signaled that the AEC was ready to begin the second phase of central power station development. Earlier in 1951, the AEC had extended its initial invitation to utilities and other interested industries to participate in a joint study of building dual-purpose reactors for producing plutonium and electricity. This opened the door for the government-industry partnership that has since characterized the U.S. civilian reactor development program.

The second phase of U.S. nuclear power development was marked by successes in the AEC's test programs, and the beginning of government/industry cooperation that would eventually make utility-owned nuclear power plants possible. The year 1953 saw the dramatic success of the S1W submarine prototype reactor that was the proof of engineering feasibility for pressurized water reactors. Other experiments at the National Reactor Testing Station demonstrated the feasibility of the boiling water reactor concept years earlier than had been expected. Later in 1953 the AEC announced its intent to conduct a "large-scale" nuclear power plant demonstration in a utility environment at a site on the Ohio River near Shippingport, Pennsylvania.

By 1954 the AEC had seen sufficient research progress in the civilian applications of nuclear technology to warrant encouraging private enterprise and international cooperation in future development activities. The Commission convinced President Eisenhower of this and he then persuaded Congress to pass the Atomic Energy Act of 1954. This new law made major changes in that it permitted private ownership of nuclear reactors, leasing of nuclear fuels for private use, and industrial access to classified data needed for nuclear power development. Furthermore, it contained provisions for encouraging the international development of nuclear power.

At the ceremony for the dedication of EBR-I as a National Historical Landmark, President Lyndon Johnson and AEC Chairman Glenn T. Seaborg examine one of the light bulbs from the first use of atomic power for electricity. (Courtesy of Argonne National Laboratory)

To implement the domestic provisions of the Atomic Energy Act of 1954, Congress and the AEC agreed on a framework for sharing the costs of nuclear power projects between government and industry. In 1955, the AEC announced the Power Demonstration Reactor Program, with invitations to participate in the first round of demonstrations of plants in the range of 75 to 110 megawatts of electric power [75 to 110 MW(e)]. Three responses were accepted and two other projects were initiated without financial assistance from the federal government. Later that year invitations were issued to participate in a second round of development projects targeted at plants in the 5- to 40-MW(e) range, with the hope of interesting smaller utilities. Four projects were chosen, and when two of these were canceled, two other projects were added. The third round of PDRP projects was not announced until 1957, with the target range being 20- to 60-MW(e) plants. Again four projects were undertaken.

Types of Reactors

A reactor can be characterized by type of fuel, moderator, and coolant. The fuel is usually enriched in U-235, the fissile isotope of uranium. Depending on the type of reactor, the enrichment of the uranium can vary from natural (0.7%) to 93%. In a closed fuel cycle, plutonium bred from U-238 can be blended with the uranium to increase the effective enrichment. Essentially all reactors produce some plutonium; in today's power reactors, plutonium produced and then fissioned in place provides a significant fraction of the power. Nuclear fuel may be a ceramic such as uranium oxide or it may be metallic alloy such as uranium-zirconium. Fuel may be very dense or it can be finely dispersed in a refractory matrix such as graphite.

The purpose of the moderator is to bring the neutrons into thermal equilibrium with the atoms in the reactor core. That is the condition that maximizes the probability of U-235 fission relative to parasitic absorption or leakage of the neutrons. Even though neutrons carry away only a tiny fraction of the energy of the fission event that releases them, their final energy is only about one-millionth of their initial energy in a thermal reactor. Ordinary water (often called "light" water), heavy water, beryllium, and graphite are typical moderators. Water is efficient because a neutron can lose all of its extra energy in a single collision with a hydrogen nucleus, but with water the fraction of parasitically absorbed neutrons is higher than desirable. If absorption is a major consideration, heavy water, which is simply water made with deuterium, a rare isotope of hydrogen, can be used. Graphite reactors are large because many collisions with carbon must occur before a neutron can reach thermal equilibrium. Breeder reactors are called "fast" because they have no effective moderator, hence the neutrons never lose all their energy. Fissions caused by high-energy neutrons result in a larger average number of neutrons being released. Fast neutrons also cause U-238 to fission in a small, but significant fraction of reactions, releasing still more neutrons. Breeder reactors are designed to absorb these extra neutrons in U-238 to breed plutonium fuel.

In light water reactors the coolant and the moderator are one and the same. Water-cooled reactors require a high system pressure to raise the boiling point of the water and keep it at the temperatures required for an efficient power plant. Helium or carbon dioxide is the usual choice for a gas coolant. Gases are not as efficient as liquids for removing heat, but since there is no concern about boiling, gas-cooled reactors are capable of the improved thermal efficiency that comes with high-temperature operation. Liquid metals such as sodium are very efficient at removing and storing heat, and they boil at very high temperature. Sodium has the added advantage of being noncorrosive, but it is incompatible with water—a design challenge for steam generators.

The projects selected for the Power Demonstration Reactor Program were remarkable in their diversity. The concepts included pressurized water, sodium graphite, fast breeder, organic cooled, boiling water, boiling water with external superheating, heavy-water moderated pressure-tube types, and high-temperature gas-cooled types. Even more concepts were being proposed or tested in experimental facilities, including aqueous homogeneous, fused salt, fluidized bed, slurry, and gas-cooled breeder systems. Obviously, not all these concepts have been successful. Only two, the pressurized water reactors and the boiling water reactors, have been extensively deployed in the United States. The fast breeder and the high-temperature gas-cooled reactor concepts have been in an extended development status, holding open the possibility for future deployment.

Starting with Shippingport in 1957, the demonstration reactors began to connect to the nation's electrical grid. Experience with these plants and further technical breakthroughs at the research facilities marked the third phase of the AEC's development program. Although most of the demonstration plants were technically successful, they did not produce electricity that was economically competitive with electricity generated by fossil fuel plants. An AEC assessment in 1960 led to two goals—demonstration of economically viable nuclear power by 1968 and the longer term development of an economical breeder reactor.

An AEC assessment in 1960 led to two goals— demonstration of economically viable nuclear power by 1968 and the longer term development of an economical breeder reactor.

Early results from the Power Demonstration Reactor Program confirmed that larger reactors would be necessary to compete with fossil fuels. No market was ever established for the small plants. An order in 1963 by Jersey Central Power and Light for a 620-MW(e) General Electric (GE) boiling water reactor plant is credited with being the breakthrough in commercialization of nuclear power in the United States. A wave of contracts followed for fixed-price, "turnkey" plants, in which the reactor vendor was responsible for completion of the entire generating station. However, unexpected cost overruns brought an end to the turnkey era in 1966. Thereafter, responsibility for construction of a plant was shared among the utility, the reactor manufacturer, an architect/engineering firm, and a construction firm, although a single company occasionally performed more than one of these functions. Limiting the scope of involvement of the reactor vendors made it possible for smaller companies, such as Babcock and Wilcox (B&W) and Combustion Engineering (C-E), to join GE and

Shippingport became the United States' first nuclear power station to generate commercial electricity in 1957. (Courtesy of Westinghouse Electric Corporation)

Westinghouse in what had become a true commercial marketplace. In 1966, 20 nuclear electric generating stations were ordered; 30 in 1967.

Pressurized Water Reactors

On December 2, 1957, fifteen years to the day of the first controlled nuclear chain reaction at Stagg Field, a team of scientists, engineers, and technicians brought the reactor of the Shippingport Atomic Power Station to its first critical condition and launched commercial nuclear power in the United States. In 1992, fifty years after CP-1, PWRs are the leading reactor type, with 74 PWR plants operating in the United States.

But in the earliest days of civilian nuclear power development, PWRs, or for that matter any type of light (ordinary water as opposed to "heavy") -water-cooled system, seemed like a poor bet to finish first. Technical problems handicapped the PWR concept: the relatively high neutron absorption rate of

Admiral Hyman D. Rickover.
(Courtesy of Argonne National
Laboratory)

water; the lack of an adequate fuel design; and the absence of high-temperature, high-pressure, corrosion-resistant components. But technical progress came fast. Confidence was high in those early days; often the next phase was committed before positive results from the previous step were demonstrated. One successful development after another paved the way for the selection of the PWR for the first commercial demonstration of nuclear power.

The road to Shippingport began in Oak Ridge, Tennessee, in 1946 when Farrington Daniels proposed a joint government/industry project to build an experimental power reactor at the Clinton Laboratories. Daniels was a chemist who had been director of the Chicago Metallurgical Laboratory during the final months of World War II. The idea behind making the project a joint effort of the laboratories, industry, and the armed forces was that each participant could take away the technology needed for specific applications. Among the people sent to participate once agreement was reached were John Simpson of Westinghouse, Harry Stevens of General Electric, and Hyman D. Rickover of the U.S. Navy. The effort became known as the Daniels Pile Project. The reactor to be built was based on a beryllium-moderated, helium-cooled, high-temperature concept. This proved to be overly ambitious for what was to be a short-term, loosely organized project.

After the AEC was formed, work on the Daniels Pile was halted. But by then, a study of the feasibility of developing a reactor for submarine propulsion was well along. Rickover had taken advantage of the lack of direction in the pile project to persuade a group to work on his dream of nuclear propulsion. The study identified two reactor concepts that would be compact enough to fit within a submarine hull—pressurized water and liquid-metal types. The pressurized water concept had been proposed by Alvin Weinberg, leader of the Oak Ridge physicists, in 1946. Liquid sodium coolant had been under consideration for the development of breeder reactors. Based on experience from the Manhattan Project, the wisdom of pursuing parallel paths was recognized.

In 1948, the AEC transferred responsibility for developing the submarine propulsion reactor to Argonne National Laboratory (ANL), and later awarded a contract to Westinghouse to design and build the Submarine Thermal

Reactor (STR) prototype, since renamed S1W. The design work was done at the Bettis Atomic Power Laboratory, which is still operated by Westinghouse. In 1950, General Electric, operator of Knolls Atomic Power Laboratory, reached an agreement to design and build the liquid-metal naval reactor.

The selection of PWR technology for the development of naval submarine propulsion proved to be a momentous decision for the future of civilian nuclear power development. Many technical accomplishments between 1948 and 1953 made the success of the PWR concept possible: highly enriched nuclear fuel, pure zirconium crystal bar from which to make cladding for the fuel, materials resistant to the corrosive effects of high-temperature, high-pressure water, improved reactor physics analysis methods and data, and successful development of a large number of necessary components. The S1W prototype was an unqualified success. By June 1953, the reactor and associated systems had completed a long test at power to demonstrate submarine propulsion feasibility. Although it produced mechanical rather than electrical energy, this was the first demonstration of sustained production of a significant amount of useful energy by a nuclear reactor. In July, a parallel design activity at Bettis to develop a nuclear plant for an aircraft carrier was canceled, and the effort was converted into the development of a central station nuclear plant. The following year the nuclear submarine USS *Nautilus* began operation that continued until 1980. The successful operation of the *Nautilus* was a clear and dramatic demonstration of the safety and reliability of nuclear power. No longer a questionable contender, by 1954 PWR technology was the front-runner for the demonstration of civilian nuclear power.

In March 1954, the AEC selected a group of companies to build the Shippingport Atomic Power Station at Shippingport, Pennsylvania. Duquesne Light Company was to be the operator and build the secondary part of the plant. Westinghouse was responsible for the reactor; the Stone & Webster Corporation provided the architect-engineering services for the nuclear portion, the Dravo Corporation performed the installation; and Burns & Roe acted

Two of the early nuclear-powered submarines, the USS *Seawolf* in front and the USS *Nautilus* in back. (Courtesy of US Navy)

as agent-constructor in building the turbine portion of the plant. The AEC assigned overall responsibility for the project to its Naval Reactors Branch, Division of Reactor Development. On December 23, 1958, the Shippingport Atomic Power Station delivered its full power of 60 MW of electricity to the Pittsburgh area. The plant operated until 1982, when it became the first U.S. plant to be fully decommissioned.

Shippingport pioneered the use of uranium-dioxide fuel in a water-cooled reactor, which was considered a major technical breakthrough for the future development of PWRs. As the first central station nuclear power plant in the United States, it demonstrated important safeguards necessary in the construction and operation of a reactor facility near a large city. Near the end of its career, Shippingport was used as a demonstration test reactor for the Light Water Breeder Reactor Project, with the objective of showing that a marginal breeder could be developed with a thorium/U-233 fuel cycle.

President Dwight D. Eisenhower symbolically waving a wand in Denver to start remotely the ground breaking for the Shippingport reactor. (Courtesy of U.S. Council for Energy Awareness)

Historical Ground Breaking

John Simpson made the following remarks about the history of Shippingport at an American Nuclear Society symposium in 1982 commemorating the fortieth anniversary of the CP-1 experiment[1]:

> ... Ground was broken in September 1954. In order to spice up the ceremony, we had rigged up a high lift to be operated remotely. President Eisenhower was to wave a radioactive wand in Denver and the high lift would scoop up a load of dirt. The trial run was filmed and was to be shown on nationwide television that night as the actual ground breaking. I was told that if things didn't work right I could just start walking and keep on walking.

> Actual construction began in May 1955. The plant went critical on December 2, 1957, and produced its full power of 60 megawatts of electric on December 23, 1958, with only three loops operating—4 ½ years from a small submarine prototype reactor to a commercial generating station of reasonable size for the period and only 15 years after Stagg Field.

> Just as the Navy had decided to construct the *Nautilus* before the prototype operated, Westinghouse decided to build the next-generation central station plant before Shippingport operated. For this decision, Shippingport was the *sine qua non*.

> With the passage of the Atomic Energy Act of 1954, Westinghouse set up the Commercial Atomic Power Activity to enable it to carry out its own atomic power research and development. Most of the key people in the commercial activity had come from Bettis, having been declared surplus and not needed for some reason or other, but much of the Bettis data was unavailable because it was classified. The AEC was trying to get nuclear power moving with the demonstration program. Bill Webster headed up the Yankee Atomic Power Company, which was selected for one of these. This led to the tri-party contract: Yankee, Westinghouse, and Stone & Webster.

> The reference design was 134 megawatts, but the actual capacity was increased to 175 megawatts....

[1] John W. Simpson, "History of Shippingport," in *Historical Perspectives: Dawn of the Nuclear Age*, American Nuclear Society, La Grange Park, IL (1989).

The Yankee-Rowe PWR was part of the first round of the AEC's Power Demonstration Reactor Program. Built in Rowe, Massachusetts, Yankee started commercial operation in 1960 and was just taken out of service in 1992. With the Shippingport and Yankee-Rowe experience behind it, Westinghouse has gone on to build many PWRs around the world. In 1992, fifty Westinghouse PWRs are operating in the United States. The largest PWRs in the United States today are Houston Lighting and Power Company's two Westinghouse 1250-MW(e) plants.

Babcock and Wilcox (B&W) entered the PWR market in New York with Indian Point Unit No. 1, which operated from 1963 to 1974. Today there are seven B&W PWRs operating in the United States. Combustion Engineering (C–E) entered the PWR market with the 700-MW(e) Palisades plant in South

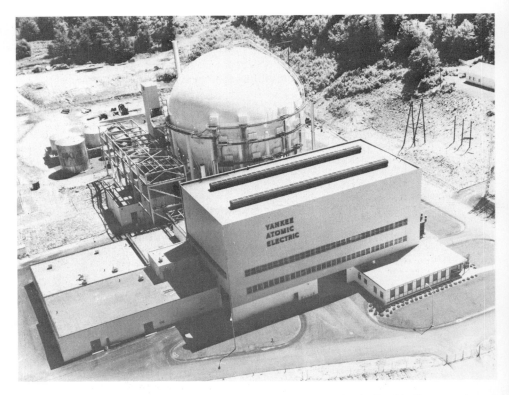

The Yankee-Rowe Nuclear Power Plant. (Courtesy of Yankee Atomic Electric Company)

Haven, Michigan, which began commercial service in 1971. Sixteen C–E PWR plants are currently in operation in the United States.

Boiling Water Reactors

Boiling water reactors do just what the name implies. Operating at approximately one-half the pressure of a PWR, the coolant water is allowed to boil within the reactor pressure vessel. The steam is separated from the water and sent directly to the turbine-generator, eliminating the need for a separate steam generator. When the BWR concept was proposed for development, this simplification was recognized for its potential economic benefit. However, it also raised two fundamental questions relative to its practicality: (1) Would the nuclear chain reaction be stable in a system in which the density of the moderator fluctuated because of the formation of steam bubbles? (2) Would transport of radioactive contamination to the turbine-generator be a difficult

The two 1250-MW(e) PWRs at the South Texas Project in Palacios, Texas. (Courtesy of Houston Lighting and Power Company)

operational problem? In addition, the BWR presented many of the same challenges as the PWR in being considered for commercialization of nuclear power.

Boiling Water Reactor Test Program

The AEC developed a program to test the principles of the BWR concept, authorizing a test facility to be constructed at the National Reactor Testing Station near EBR-I. Argonne National Laboratory, under the direction of Walter Zinn, built an experimental boiling water reactor (BORAX), which was ready to begin testing in 1953. BORAX-I, the first in the series of boiling test reactors, proved that formation of steam bubbles in the reactor core did not cause an instability problem. In fact, the system proved to be inherently stable. In 1955 a turbine-generator was added to BORAX-II, a larger and higher pressure version of BORAX-I, and tests with BORAX-III demonstrated that turbine contamination would not be a significant problem in BWRs. However, BORAX-III is best remembered for producing steam-generated electricity in sufficient quantity to light the town of Arco, Idaho, the night of July 17, 1955— an event Arco still celebrates today. These landmark experiments provided the technical foundation for the first boiling water nuclear power plants. Subsequent BORAX tests addressed the possibility of providing higher steam temperatures by using nuclear superheat in conjunction with a boiling water reactor.

THE ARCO ADVERTISER

Serving America's Newest Atomic Center   Voice of the Lost River Country Since 1909   10 Cents Per Copy

VOL. XLVI—Number 24   Arco, Butte County, Idaho   Friday, August 12, 1955

Arco First City In United States Lighted By Atomic Power

At 11:55 p.m. on Sunday, July 17, Arco became the first city in the United States, and perhaps the free world, to receive its electrical power from atomic energy. This was revealed officially early this morning in a dispatch from Geneva, Switzerland where the Atoms For Peace conference is in session. While it was rumored at the time that the city had been lighted by atomic energy, no announcement was made until 1 a.m. today. The pictures above briefly tell the story of how Arco was on atomic power for about an hour. In the picture at the left, Mr'ice Novick, Argonne National Laborat-

ory engineer, turns a valve to release steam from Borax reactor into the turbine which drives 3,500 kilowatt capacity generator shown at the right of picture. The Borax reactor is located at the AEC site. In the next picture is a schematic drawing of the power network used in supplying Arco with electricity from the Borax generator at NRTS. Arco is served by two different lines of the Utah Power and Light Company. An old, unused section of power line, represented by dotted line on drawing, connects the NRTS with one of these lines at the point between Arco and Howe. Throwing a switch at the NRTS (lower magnified circle on drawing) cut Borax off con-

ventional power and let it provide electricity to Arco's alternate line. Another switch (upper magnified circle) cut Arco off conventional power and onto nuclear power. Dotted line at Borax represents circuitry which enabled reactor to run on its own power, a step preliminary to taking over line load. In the picture at the right, Arco takes on an "Atomic Glow." The picture was taken from the hill at the head of Main Street. Taking late at night, the picture shows lights on Main Street and other street lights in town. (Photos by Atomic Energy Commission, Idaho Falls)

Northern District Posse Meet Here Saturday; Six Riding Clubs To Vie For Honors In Two Performances

Peep Sights

Arco On Atomic Power One Hour In Nuclear Test From Energy Produced At Experimental Reactor At AEC

Rites Held For Sidney L. Martin

Three Highway Accidents Are Reported Here

We Knew About It All The Time

Stake Old Folks Party August 24

Mrs. O. T. Jones To Son's Wedding

Patrolman Tells Rotarians High Speed, Drinking Accident Causes

District P.T.A. To Meet In Mackay

Fair Plans Are Near Completion

Arco (Idaho) newspaper announcing the lighting of the town by atomic power provided by BORAX III. (Courtesy of Argonne National Laboratory)

Experimental Boiling Water Reactor

In May 1955 ground was broken at Argonne's Illinois site for construction of the AEC's Experimental Boiling Water Reactor (EBWR). The plant was operational in December 1956. Whereas the earlier BORAX experiments demonstrated the stability and safety of the in-core boiling process, EBWR was built to demonstrate the operation of a boiling water reactor system as a central power station.

The EBWR was run in parallel with the electrical utility, Commonwealth Edison, so that data on the effect of the network characteristics on the generator, turbine, and reactor could be collected for use in designing subsequent BWR central station power plants. After successful operation at the initial rating of 5 MW(e), 20 MW total of thermal power, in the central power station mode, the system was modified to generate up to 100 MW as a demonstration of the capabilities of this reactor type. After EBWR demonstrated successful operation at 100 MW, the reactor was used in the joint ANL-Hanford Plutonium Recycle Program to obtain information on the use of plutonium as a fuel in light water reactors. In September 1965, the EBWR began

The Experimental Boiling Water Reactor. (Courtesy of Argonne National Laboratory)

Dresden 1, the first commercial boiling water reactor. (Courtesy of Commonwealth Edison)

operation at power levels up to 70 MW with plutonium as its principal fuel. EBWR was shut down in June 1967 when this final mission was completed.

Vallecitos Boiling Water Reactor

In 1956, GE moved its commercial nuclear power organization from Schenectady, New York, to San Jose, California, and soon began construction of the Vallecitos Nuclear Laboratory nearby. Construction of an experimental 5-MW(e) nuclear power plant began in June 1956; the reactor first went critical in August 1957; and full power was reached in October 1957. The AEC issued Power Reactor License No. 1 to the Vallecitos Boiling Water Reactor. The turbine-generator and related electrical facilities were owned and operated by Pacific Gas and Electric Company. GE intended to use technical results from Vallecitos in designing its first commercial plant, which had been ordered the previous year.

Dresden

Dresden, the first large-scale, utility-owned nuclear power plant, was the next logical step in BWR demonstration following the success of the EBWR experiments. Located about 50 miles southwest of Chicago, Dresden started commercial operation in 1960. The Commonwealth Edison Company owned and operated the plant. The Bechtel Corporation served as architect-engineer and constructor. Major construction work started at the Dresden site in June 1957. The reactor, which went critical for the first time in October 1959, reached full power in June 1960. The initial net electrical output was 184 MW(e), but performance exceeded expectations and the power rating was increased to 210 MW(e) in 1961.

GE Selects the BWR for Commercial Nuclear Power

On the occasion of the fiftieth anniversary of the discovery of fission, Bertram Wolfe spoke of GE's entry into the nuclear power business and the significance of Dresden[2]:

... In 1954 after the Atoms for Peace Program was initiated by President Eisenhower, GE set up a study group to determine if and how it should participate in the new technology of peaceful nuclear power. GE was already involved in the nuclear field through its management of the Hanford Works in Washington State and the Knolls Atomic Power Laboratory (KAPL) in Schenectady, New York. The study group concluded that nuclear power was a technology in which GE should participate commercially. The choice of reactor type became an issue. The graphite-moderated, tube-type, water-cooled reactor was placed high on the list because of GE experience with this type of reactor at Hanford. The light water reactor, in particular the Boiling Water Reactor (BWR), because of its simple steam cycle and the success of the BORAX and Experimental Boiling Water Reactor programs at Argonne National Laboratory, was considered a second possibility. The third alternative was the liquid-metal-cooled reactor based on KAPL experience....

Further evaluations by the GE study group concluded that the graphite reactor would be too expensive, and that the BWR would have economic and operating benefits relative to both the graphite reactor and the PWR. Thus, the BWR was accepted by GE as its future nuclear product line.

In 1955, GE and Commonwealth Edison Company reached agreement to build the Dresden-1 Boiling Water Nuclear Reactor Power Plant. There were several unique points to this agreement. The two companies agreed that if nuclear power was to succeed in this country, it had to succeed as a private enterprise without government interference. To this end, the Dresden-1 project was funded by CECo and a group of associated utilities, and by GE. It was the only nuclear power project of the fifties set up with no government financial participation. The project was a turnkey project with GE agreeing to build and start up the 180-MW(e) BWR for a fixed price of $45 million.

The Dresden-1 project was the start of the peaceful nuclear power business in GE and the introduction of the commercial BWR to the nation and the world....

[2]Bertram Wolfe, "The BWR and the Start of the Nuclear Power Era," in *Proceedings of 50 Years with Nuclear Fission,* American Nuclear Society, La Grange Park, IL (1989).

Demonstration of Other Reactor Technologies

Although only the PWR and BWR have been commercially successful in the United States, the early history of U.S. reactor development is rich with innovative experiments at the AEC's test facilities and intrepid demonstrations in the Power Demonstration Reactor Program. The AEC's test program and its power demonstration program were linked, but demonstration projects often proceeded boldly before tests were fully completed, and usually involved significant extrapolation in size. There is not room to mention all the

AEC tests here, nor is there room to do justice to the demonstration of the alternative reactor technologies. But it is worth recounting part of the story to understand just how different the climate was in those early days. Men and women of courage and vision in the AEC, the national laboratories, the utilities, and the manufacturing companies worked together to demonstrate technology that would have seemed like science fiction only a generation earlier.

The U.S. monopoly on enriched uranium opened up a far broader range of reactor concepts than could be considered by most other nations before the

The interior of the Hallam Nuclear Plant. (Courtesy of Rockwell International Corporation)

Atomic Energy Act of 1954 was passed. Reactors requiring from 1 to 93% enrichment in U-235 were considered and built. Designs were motivated by the search for higher thermal efficiency, lower system pressure, ability to stay on line continuously, and better utilization of uranium resources. Many of the reactor technology concepts were first tried at the AEC's National Reactor Testing Station, but experiments were also going on at Los Alamos, Oak Ridge, Argonne, and some private test facilities, such as GE's Vallecitos Nuclear Facility.

With the success of the S1W prototype, the *Nautilus,* and Shippingport, the importance of the naval reactor program to development of the PWR is clear. The Navy also successfully demonstrated sodium-cooled technology with the Sodium Intermediate Reactor (SIR) prototype. This technology was developed by the Knolls Atomic Power Laboratory and installed in the nuclear submarine *Seawolf,* which operated from 1957 to 1959. Following a problem with sodium leakage into the *Seawolf's* steam reheaters, the Navy abandoned development of sodium-cooled reactors for propulsion. However, there was still interest in a power station with the high-efficiency, low-pressure system possible with sodium coolant. In 1957, Atomics International started operation of the AEC's Sodium Reactor Experiment (SRE) at the Santa Susana, California, facility. Experience with sodium technology was also gained through the AEC's breeder reactor program.

> Designs were motivated by the search for higher thermal efficiency, lower system pressure, ability to stay on line continuously, and better utilization of uranium resources.

A sodium-cooled, graphite-moderated reactor was one of the technologies chosen for demonstration in the first round of the AEC's demonstration program. The 75-MW(e) Hallam Nuclear Power Facility was built at Hallam, Nebraska, by Atomics International for the AEC and the Consumers Public Power District. The facility started operation in 1962; failures of several system components led to shutdown in 1964. Development of this type of technology was subsequently dropped.

The desire for safety and simplicity of low-pressure systems also led to experiments with organic coolants. The Organic Moderated Reactor Experiment (OMRE) was conducted at the National Reactor Testing Station. This concept was included in the AEC's second round of demonstrations involving small plants at small electric utilities. The Piqua plant—11-MW(e), organic-cooled, organic-moderated—went critical in 1963. Built by Atomics International and Aerojet General, the AEC funded 99.3% of the cost of this plant at

The organically cooled and moderated Piqua reactor in Piqua, Ohio. (Courtesy of Rockwell International Corporation)

Piqua, Ohio. Operation with the organic coolant, terphenyl, proved difficult, leading to the plant's shutdown in 1965. Some research with organic coolants continued, but no other plants of this type were built in the United States.

The quest for higher thermal efficiency led to BWR demonstration projects with superheated steam systems. The BORAX-V experiments demonstrated the possibility of nuclear superheat. In 1959, construction started on the 59-MW(e) Pathfinder BWR plant in Sioux Falls, South Dakota. Part of the second round of the demonstration program, this project, built by Allis-Chalmers, included external coal-fired superheaters. Pathfinder operated from 1964 to 1968. The 17-MW(e) Boiling Nuclear Superheat Station (BONUS), a BWR with nuclear superheat, was built in Puerto Rico by Combustion Engineering and the General Nuclear Engineering Corporation. BONUS operated from 1964 to 1968, when it was shut down because of continuing operational difficulties.

Only one heavy water reactor was built as a part of the demonstration program—the Carolina Virginia Tube Reactor (CVTR). This plant, using heavy water moderator and coolant, was built by Westinghouse as part of the AEC's third round of demonstrations. The 17-MW(e) reactor operated from 1964 to 1967.

Oak Ridge National Laboratory was the center for development of the homogeneous reactor concepts. The goals for these concepts were continuous processing for removal of fission products, continuous addition of fuel to avoid refueling shutdowns, and simplified reactor controls. The aqueous Homogeneous Reactor Experiment was built to conduct research and development on the concept. The program was never able to overcome the corrosion problems that were encountered and was eventually dropped. In its place, a fused salt technology program with similar goals continued. The molten salt concept had the additional advantage of reduced system pressure. However, materials and potential operational problems also led to this concept being abandoned. No demonstration plant of either type was ever built.

Two demonstration plants were built for which development of the technologies continued, but true commercialization was never realized—the high-temperature gas-cooled reactor (HTGR) and the sodium-cooled fast breeder reactor, now better known as the liquid-metal-cooled reactor (LMR). The HTGR offered substantial improvement in thermal efficiency and the possibility of high-temperature industrial heat applications. The LMR held promise of higher thermal efficiency than LWRs, the simplicity and safety of a low-pressure system, and an enormous improvement in uranium resource utilization. The two technologies differed substantially in the relative importance of the demonstration program. For the HTGR, the importance of early success in the demonstration program was overriding. Demonstration came at a relatively early stage in development of LMR technology; lasting achievements were made in the test facilities of the AEC and its successor agencies, the Energy Research and Development Administration and the Department of Energy (DOE).

High-Temperature Gas-Cooled Reactors

The concept of a graphite-moderated, gas-cooled power reactor dates back to the Manhattan Project. The Daniels Pile work in the pre-AEC days focused on an advanced gas-cooled reactor, albeit beryllium moderated. A gas-cooled reactor experiment was built and operated by the Aerojet General Corporation at the National Reactor Testing Station. Gas-cooled reactors were operating successfully in Europe. But the big push for a gas-cooled power reactor in the United States came with the selection of the HTGR as one of the plants to be built in the third round of the AEC's demonstration program. The contract for Peach Bottom 1 was signed in 1959 between the AEC, General Atomics, and the

The 40-MW(e) Peach Bottom HTGR. (Courtesy of General Atomics)

Philadelphia Electric Company. Full power for the 40-MW(e) unit was achieved in 1967.

The fuel design of the original Peach Bottom core incorporated no room for fission gas expansion, resulting in cracking in 90 graphite sleeves of the 804 fuel elements. Nevertheless, the circulating contamination was less than 10% of the design value. With improvements in the fuel design of the second reactor core, radiation doses to plant workers were a factor of 50 lower than for comparable jobs in LWR plants. Peach Bottom 1 had an overall availability of 66% before it was shut down in 1974. The success of the Peach Bottom 1 demonstration encouraged utilities to commercialize the technology.

The 330-MW(e) Fort Saint Vrain HTGR. (Courtesy of General Atomics)

However, the success of Peach Bottom 1 did not carry over to the next HTGR demonstration, the Fort St. Vrain Power Station. Fort St. Vrain was the AEC's next-to-last power reactor demonstration. The contract between General Atomics and the Public Service Company of Colorado was signed during the latter stages of construction of Peach Bottom 1. Construction for the 330-MW(e) plant was approved in 1968. Besides the significant scale-up in size, the plant included a number of first-of-a-kind features.

The problems encountered with Fort St. Vrain operation are indicative of the risk associated with the scale-up of any large industrial process. The initial major problem was movement of the massive fuel columns caused by an uneven temperature distribution. Delays while the problem was identified—and a solution worked out and approved—caused the full-power demonstration to be put off until 1981, five years after the scheduled startup. Changes in the NRC rules for nuclear plants resulted in a number of forced changes before construction could be completed. The biggest impact resulted from design deficiencies in the circulator for the helium coolant, which had water-lubricated bearings. Over the life of the plant, more than 1000 gallons of water entered the reactor system, causing long shutdowns for repairs to a number of components. Fort St. Vrain ended its career having achieved only a 15% capacity factor.

The Fort St. Vrain plant was shut down in 1989, a disappointment following the success of Peach Bottom 1 and gas-cooled reactors in Europe, particularly the United Kingdom. During the late 1960s and 1970s, General Atomics received orders for 10 large HTGRs from U.S. utilities. Each order was eventually canceled by mutual agreement between GA and the utilities; the reasons had as much to do with such institutional issues as oversupply of electrical generating capacity as the technical problems of Fort St. Vrain. As has been the case with other reactor types that have continued development, the problems encountered in the Fort St. Vrain experience have been factored into improving the design of next-generation HTGRs.

Liquid-Metal Reactors

The liquid-metal reactor was selected for development as soon as the AEC was established in 1946, was reaffirmed in the AEC's long-range development plan in 1968, and remains as DOE's principal line of advanced reactor development today. The reason for the sustained interest in LMR technology is the potential for breeding, the only way that nuclear power can provide significant and lasting beneficial service to mankind.

Natural uranium consists of 99.3% U-238, the uranium isotope that is of little use in LWR or gas-cooled reactors. With LMRs operated in a breeding mode with plutonium fuel, more atoms of plutonium are produced by absorption in U-238 than are consumed by fission. With recycling, a breeder can not only produce enough fuel for itself, it can provide startup fuel for expanded deployment of other LMRs. If there is to be long-term, widespread use of nuclear power, the final phase of the transition from CP-1 to commercial power reactors will be the deployment of fast-breeder LMRs.

Fast reactor experiments began at Los Alamos in 1946 with the Clementine reactor, used for physics studies with unmoderated neutrons. Los Alamos also conducted one of the most novel fast reactor experiments with the Los Alamos Molten Plutonium Reactor Experiment (LAMPRE). LAMPRE was a 1-MW system of molten plutonium and iron, which operated between 1961 and 1965.

With opening of the National Reactor Testing Station, attention shifted to Experimental Breeder Reactor I, which started construction in 1949. EBR-I was built under the direction of Walter Zinn, who had been responsible for the day-shift crew that constructed the CP-1. The reactor reached its full power of 1.1 MW in late 1951. Modifications were made to include power generation equipment, and on December 20, 1951, EBR-I steam produced the first-ever

The 19-MW(e) EBR-II power plant and its associated fuel cycle facility. (Courtesy of Argonne National Laboratory)

demonstration of nuclear electricity. In 1953, the AEC gave Argonne permission to start designing EBR-II.

EBR-II was built as a prototype power plant producing 19 MW(e). Full-power operation began in 1964 and continues today. Between 1964 and 1969, the EBR-II fuel was reprocessed and fabricated in an adjacent fuel cycle facility before being sent back to the reactor. Despite being continuously used for a wide variety of experiments including operational transients, EBR-II has maintained a capacity factor comparable with U.S. commercial plants.

The Southwest Experimental Fast Oxide Reactor (SEFOR) was a 20-MW experimental reactor operated between 1968 and 1972 as part of an international cooperative program involving the AEC, a group of American utility companies, General Electric, and Gesellschaft für Kernforschung of Karlsruhe, West Germany. The purpose of SEFOR was to determine the operating characteristics of a reactor with mixed plutonium-oxide/uranium-oxide fuel, but in particular to demonstrate the Doppler effect in a fast reactor with mixed-oxide fuel. (The Doppler effect is a self-limiting feature of reactors in which the fraction of neutrons absorbed in U-238 goes up as the temperature of the fuel rises, making fewer neutrons available to continue the chain reaction, and thus providing a fast-acting shutdown mechanism.)

The AEC built the large Fast Flux Test Facility (FFTF) as an irradiation test bed for fast reactor fuels and materials. Completed in 1980, this 400-MW reactor is still in operation. FFTF has operated reliably, demonstrating the high burnup achievable with mixed-oxide fuel for LMRs and the relative ease of maintenance of low-pressure liquid sodium systems.

The Fast Flux Test Facility. (Courtesy of Westinghouse Hanford Company)

In the most ambitious undertaking of the first round of the AEC Power Demonstration Reactor Program, conceptual design of the 61-MW(e) Enrico Fermi 1 sodium-cooled breeder reactor began in 1955. The plant, constructed near Detroit, Michigan, for an association of American utilities and Japanese companies, started operation in 1963. In retrospect, Fermi-1 probably represented a premature attempt to commercialize this promising technology, having been built without the experience of the smaller EBR-II prototype. A valuable design lesson was learned in 1966 when flow blockage of a fuel assembly resulted in some local fuel melting. Following intense investigations and modifications, the plant was put back into service in 1970 and operated until its core load of fuel was depleted in 1971.

The final demonstration project taken on by the AEC was the Clinch River Breeder Reactor (CRBR), intended to be a 350-MW(e) successor to FFTF and EBR-II. The plant was designed through the 1970s; components were fabricated; and work at the construction site had begun in the early 1980s. But with the cost of the project appearing as though it would be an order-of-magnitude higher than the original estimate, and the uranium resource issue not pressing, Congress canceled the CRBR project in late 1983.

Artist's conception of the canceled Clinch River Breeder Reactor. (Courtesy of Oak Ridge National Laboratory)

BIBLIOGRAPHY

Alexanderson, E. P. (Ed.), et al. 1979. *Fermi-I: New Age for Nuclear Power*. American Nuclear Society, La Grange Park, IL.

Bulleris B., et al. 1967. "SEFOR Plant Design," in *Proceedings of Fast Reactors Topical Meeting*, San Francisco, American Nuclear Society, La Grange Park, IL.

Glasgow, L. E. April 1962. "Experience with SRE," *Nucleonics* 20 (4).

Hewlett, Richard G., and Francis Duncan. 1974. *Nuclear Navy*. University of Chicago Press.

Hogerton, J. F., et al. 1963. *The Atomic Energy Deskbook*. Reinhold Publishing Corporation.

Lane, J. A., and H. G. MacPherson. 1958. *Fluid Fuel Reactors*. Addison-Wesley Publishing Company.

LeClercq, Jacques. 1986. *The Nuclear Age*. Sodel.

Monnfield, P. R. 1991. *World Nuclear Power*. Reutledge.

Simpson, John W. 1989. "PWR History and Evaluation," in *Proceedings of 50 Years with Nuclear Fission*. American Nuclear Society, La Grange Park, IL.

Simpson, John W. 1989. "History of Shippingport," in *Historical Perspectives: Dawn of the Nuclear Age*. American Nuclear Society, La Grange Park, IL.

Wolfe, Bertram. 1989. "The BWR and the Start of the Nuclear Power Era," in *Proceedings of 50 Years with Nuclear Fission*. American Nuclear Society, La Grange Park, IL.

Zinn, W. H., et al. 1964. *Nuclear Power, USA*. McGraw-Hill Book Company.

Windscale AGR pilecap: Checking the fuel temperature thermocouples. (Courtesy of AEA
Technology–Reactor Services, Risley)

THREE

Development of Nuclear Power Plants in Canada and Europe

In 1945, many foreign scientists returned home from their wartime assignments in North America. U.S. leaders were debating whether it would be possible at that time to separate the potential for nuclear power and propulsion from the weapons capability that had been developed in the Manhattan Project. In July 1946, the McMahon Act placed all nuclear development under civilian control by establishing both the U.S. Atomic Energy Commission (AEC) and the Joint Committee on Atomic Energy and overlaid most nuclear research and development with a blanket of secrecy. This U.S. congressional action separated the returning foreign scientists from the benefits of the American progress to which they had contributed. As a result, individual national programs were isolated for about ten years, until the first Atoms for Peace conference.

Without enriched uranium from the United States, and with uranium enrichment technology completely locked up, Western European and Canadian leaders had no choice but to consider natural uranium reactor concepts to get their nuclear development programs started. Some British, French, and Canadian scientists already had experience with moderated natural uranium piles, including CP-1. Those national programs that foresaw the need for enriched fuel viewed the independent development of an enrichment capability as a slower route than the production of plutonium, despite the difficult task of developing an effective chemical separation process. For France, the United Kingdom, and the Soviet Union, the plutonium route also represented the means to develop an independent nuclear military capability.

Canada[1]

Canada alone seized on the potential of the natural uranium reactor for its long-term nuclear development program. Canadian scientists concentrated on research, including some of the earliest applications of radiation therapy. Without a need for plutonium or highly enriched uranium, and with expertise developed through experience with heavy water research reactors, Canada developed the successful pressurized heavy water reactor that is known as CANDU (*CAN*adian *D*euterium *U*ranium reactor).

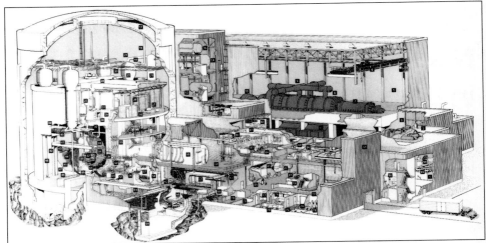

CANDU 600-MW(e) reactor. (Courtesy of AECL–CANDU Pub. & Gov. Communications)

CANDU Reactors

CANDUs use heavy water for both cooling and moderation. Because they operate using natural uranium, CANDU reactors are quite large. To avoid constructing very large high-pressure vessels, a system of pressure tubes was developed in which only the coolant water is under pressure, not the moderator. The heavy water moderator is contained in a large tank called a *calandria,* which has several hundred tubes running through it. The fuel bundles and coolant are in horizontal pressure tubes within the calandria tubes, an arrangement that allows the reactor to be refueled while at power and still connected to the grid. With this advantage, CANDUs have the potential for operating with a high capacity factor. On the down side, CANDUs operate at a relatively low temperature, resulting in a lower thermodynamic efficiency than LWRs. As enriched uranium became available for power reactors, it was demonstrated that CANDUs could be made more compact and have improved operating characteristics if the uranium oxide pellets were enriched to slightly more than 1% in U-235.

---

[1]Drawn extensively from *AECL 1991 Annual Review*, Atomic Energy of Canada Ltd. (1991).

In the late 1930s, Canadian scientists began their country's nuclear research by experimenting with fission at the Ottawa laboratories of the National Research Council. By early in World War II, a research group in Canada was considering the effectiveness of graphite and heavy water as potential moderators to sustain a chain reaction in natural uranium. In 1942, this group, led by George Laurence, was joined by a Cambridge team of scientists, led by Hans von Halban, one of Joliot-Curie's Paris colleagues. The Cambridge group brought along most of the world's supply of heavy water, which Norway had loaned to the United Kingdom.[2] Heavy water appeared likely to be the more effective moderator, but was difficult and expensive to obtain, whereas graphite of adequate purity was more readily available. Experiments with both materials had already taken place in Canada, the United Kingdom, and the United States.

There was a series of high-level meetings, agreements, and understandings between the British and Americans throughout the duration of the war. However, the American concern for maintaining secrecy in view of the mixed-European nature of the British-Canadian effort, misunderstandings about supplies, and political differences limited the degree of information exchange for considerable periods. Eventually, in April 1944, agreement was reached on the design and construction of a heavy-water-moderated reactor in Canada by a joint British and Canadian team led by John Cockcroft, a British physicist. This agreement initiated a flow of information, supplies, and other help from the United States to the project that established the Chalk River Laboratory at a wilderness site on the Ottawa River.

AECL was created to conduct research and development into the peaceful uses of nuclear science and technology.

Thus, Canada became the only nation besides the United States to start nuclear development during the war.

On September 5, 1945, the Chalk River international scientific team started up the Zero Energy Experimental Pile (ZEEP), the first nuclear reactor outside the United States. It provided information for the design of an advanced research reactor, the National Research Experimental (NRX) reactor, which began operating two years later.

In 1951, the Chalk River scientists started work on a new, world-class research reactor, the National Research Universal (NRU) reactor. NRU was designed to allow more experiments and to back up NRX in the production of

[2]B. Goldschmidt, *The Atomic Complex,* American Nuclear Society, La Grange Park, IL (1982).

ZEEP (Zero Energy Experimental Pile), the first nuclear reactor outside the United States, was started up September 5, 1945, at Chalk River, Ontario. It was heavy-water-moderated and was used to assist in the design of the NRX. (Courtesy of AECL–Research)

NRX (National Research Experimental) reactor began operating at Chalk River Laboratory on July 22, 1947. By 1949, it was operating at 20 MW(t) and was used for basic research in neutron behavior and for assessing neutron fluxes and nuclei cross sections. (Courtesy of AECL–Research)

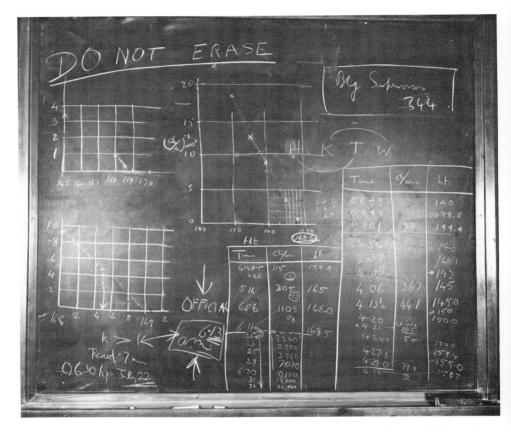

During the startup of the NRX reactor, this blackboard was set up near the control room for senior staff to be kept apprised of progress. W. B. Lewis recorded the readings as periodically telephoned from the control room. (Courtesy of AECL–Research)

radioisotopes, which were gaining importance in a number of fields, including medicine. Both NRU and NRX are still operating. That same year, the world's first cobalt therapy machine was installed at Victoria Hospital in London, Ontario, to treat cancer patients with gamma radiation from cobalt-60 produced in NRX.

On April 1, 1952, Prime Minister Louis St. Laurent established Chalk River Laboratories and its personnel as the heart of a new Crown corporation, Atomic Energy of Canada Limited (AECL), under the direction of President C. J. Mackenzie and Scientific Vice-President W. B. Lewis. AECL was created to conduct research and development into the peaceful uses of nuclear science and technology. The new company suffered a major setback when in December of its first year of operation an accident at NRX released significant

C. J. Mackenzie and W. B. Lewis, the first president and the first scientific vice-president, respectively, of Atomic Energy of Canada Limited, at the unveiling of the ZEEP historic plaque in 1975. (Courtesy of AECL–Research)

radioactivity inside the laboratory. Some 14 months passed before the reactor resumed operation.

Within two years AECL, in partnership with Ontario Hydro and Canadian General Electric, decided to enter the electricity generating arena with the 25-MW(e) Nuclear Power Demonstration (NPD) plant at Rolphton, Ontario, on the Ottawa River. The reactor used pressurized heavy water and natural uranium, a concept that was to define the Canadian program in the years ahead. As the three companies worked on plans for NPD, AECL completed the NRU reactor at Chalk River, starting it up November 3, 1957, to produce neutrons for research and radioisotopes for various applications. Even before completion of the Rolphton unit, AECL and Ontario Hydro decided to build a 200-MW(e) commercial prototype at Douglas Point on Lake Huron.

Deuterium

The well-known chemical formula for ordinary water is H_2O, with the H representing the most abundant isotope (H-1) of hydrogen, protium, whose nucleus is a single proton. Heavy water, D_2O, is made from the deuterium isotope (H-2) of hydrogen.

The Glace Bay, Nova Scotia, heavy water plant. It had a target capacity of 180 tonnes/yr. (Courtesy of AECL–Research)

Deuterium has a nucleus containing a proton and a neutron. The chemical properties of the two hydrogen isotopes are the same, but deuterium has twice the mass of protium.

Deuterium exists in nature in a ratio of only 1 to 6500 with protium. Normal water can be enriched in D_2O by a number of energy-intensive processes. The primary method for the production of heavy water is called the *dual-temperature water-hydrogen sulfide exchange process,* which is based on the temperature dependence of the exchange rate between deuterium in hydrogen sulfide and protium in water. In commercial facilities, the H_2S process is typically used to enrich the water to approximately 25% D_2O. Because the boiling points of heavy and light water differ slightly, distillation is used to produce the final product, which is approximately 99.75% D_2O.

Douglas Point, the 208-MW(e) plant which ran successfully from 1968 to 1984. Designed by AECL, it was operated by Ontario Hydro. (Courtesy of AECL–CANDU and Ontario Hydro)

Despite the emphasis on commercial technology, AECL realized that research was vital to its long-term success, and in 1959, the corporation decided to build a second research center, Whiteshell Laboratories, at Pinawa, Manitoba. That same year, the commercial products operation that AECL had taken over from Eldorado Mining and Refining in 1952, was moved to Kanata, Ontario. The Commercial Products Division eventually became Nordion International Inc., producing radioisotopes marketed in Canada and abroad. The company was sold to the private sector in 1991.

As the 1960s unfolded, AECL and Ontario Hydro continued work on the Douglas Point reactor while finishing up NPD at Rolphton. The key milestone for AECL came in 1962, when NPD was completed and started to feed Canada's first nuclear-generated electricity to the Ontario grid. The next year, AECL and Ontario Hydro planned a new plant, a two-unit, fully commercial [1000-MW(e)] station at Pickering on Lake Ontario. Over the next 24 years, Pickering grew to four and, finally, eight units. The 200-MW(e) commercial prototype reactor at Douglas Point was commissioned in 1966.

In attempts to improve the CANDU's thermal efficiency, AECL engineers studied alternative designs, including higher temperature organic coolant and boiling light water coolant. In 1965, scientists at the Whiteshell Laboratories

WR-1 research reactor at the Whiteshell Laboratory in Pinawa, Manitoba. It was a heavy-water-moderated, organic-cooled reactor with a power level of 60 MW(t) , and it did not exhibit any of the "coking" problems observed in other organic reactors. WR-1 went critical in 1965 and ran until 1985. After 1978, its output was used to heat the site. (Courtesy of AECL–Research)

started up Canada's first organically cooled research reactor, WR-1, which, in contrast to the U.S. experience with organically cooled reactors, performed satisfactorily. In 1966, work started on Gentilly-1, a 250-MW(e) prototype boiling light-water-cooled, heavy-water-moderated CANDU at the Hydro-Quebec plant near Trois Rivieres in Quebec. The plant did not perform to expectations and was eventually replaced by Gentilly-2, a 685-MW(e) CANDU 6 power plant.

With the Pickering station still under construction in 1968, AECL and Ontario Hydro announced plans to build a four-reactor generating station on the Bruce Peninsula, adjacent to the Douglas Point commercial prototype. Like

Darlington Station, Ontario, under construction. It has a (4 × 881-MW(e)) capacity and is the latest in the CANDU series. (Courtesy of AECL–CANDU and Ontario Hydro)

Pickering, the Bruce site eventually housed eight reactors, although these were in the 800- to 900-MW(e) range.

Also in 1968, AECL began to market CANDU internationally. Small CANDU reactors were already being built in India and Pakistan (the former patterned after the commercial prototype at Douglas Point) under agreements signed in 1963–64. As the 1970s opened, the first two Pickering units and KANUPP, the CANDU station built in Pakistan, began producing electricity. By 1973, with Unit 4 in operation, the Pickering station was generating more electricity than any other nuclear power station in the world. That same year, the Rajasthan 1 CANDU reactor was completed in India. However, Canadian nonproliferation policy suffered a setback in 1974, following India's detonation of a nuclear device. All nuclear shipments to India were suspended and cooperation with the Indian Atomic Energy Commission was terminated.

In 1974, AECL sold its first large reactor abroad, to Argentina. Meanwhile, Ontario Hydro started preparing for its second four-unit station at Pickering. In 1976, the second major CANDU export order, this time by South Korea, was signed. Over the next four years, power started flowing from the Bruce station, AECL began a major research program to develop a permanent solution for disposing of nuclear fuel waste, and preparations were started for construction of a five-unit CANDU station in Romania.

The only significant technical setback of the 1980s occurred when pressure tube problems caused unexpected repairs and delays in service at the Pickering station. Many of the previous decade's efforts bore fruit. AECL constructed an underground laboratory at Lac du Bonnet in Manitoba as a major component of its waste disposal research program. CANDU 6 reactors in New Brunswick, Quebec, South Korea, and Argentina began producing power, as did the last four units at the Bruce plant.

United Kingdom

British scientists were heavily involved in basic atomic research before the war. Their participation in the Manhattan Project and in the research going on in Canada put the United Kingdom in position to begin nuclear development soon after the war. Operating with the same resource handicap as other nations, the United Kingdom turned to large graphite-moderated natural uranium reactors to launch its nuclear program. British engineers soon mastered gas-cooled reactor (GCR) technology for electricity production, and the United Kingdom surged to the top of the world in nuclear electricity generation during the late 1950s. The United Kingdom was the only country to be successful in large-scale deployment of GCRs. By the early 1970s, British engineers were in the thick of the race to develop the

> Although the McMahon Act forced the United Kingdom to start independent development of nuclear reactors, much British experience had been gained with the cooperative development at Chalk River in Canada.

breeder. With pressure to use its coal resources, and more recently oil and gas from the North Sea, the UK has taken a more deliberate approach to expanding its nuclear generating capacity in recent years. This allowed time for reevalu-

Sir John Cockcroft, first director of (Atomic Energy) Research (1946) and an original member of the UKAEA (1954). (Courtesy of AEA Technology–Harwell)

Sir William (later Lord) Penney, chief superintendent of armament research (1947), an original member of the UKAEA (1954), and Chairman of the UKAEA in 1964. (Courtesy of AEA Technology–Harwell)

Sir Christopher (later Lord) Hinton, deputy controller of atomic energy for materials (1946), an original member of the UKAEA (1954), and Chairman of the Central Electricity Generating Board in 1957. (Courtesy of AEA Technology–Harwell)

ation of which reactor technology would be selected for future deployment. After much debate, the United Kingdom eventually turned away from its domestic gas-cooled reactors and selected pressurized water reactor (PWR) technology for its next generation of power stations.

The United Kingdom entered the nuclear reactor field in 1945 by setting up the Atomic Energy Research Establishment (AERE) at Harwell under John Cockcroft. The priority at that time was to develop an independent nuclear deterrent, i.e., a military program. In 1946, a fissile material production group was established at Risley under Christopher Hinton. Armament research was established in 1947 under William Penney at what became the Atomic Weapons Research Establishment at Aldermaston.

Although the McMahon Act forced the United Kingdom to start independent development of nuclear reactors, much British experience had been gained with the cooperative development at Chalk River in Canada. Without an existing uranium separation plant and no supply of heavy water, the quickest route to a nuclear capability was through production of plutonium in a natural uranium graphite pile. This decision set the basis for the U.K. nuclear power production program through 1978.

GLEEP

The first U.K. research reactor, GLEEP (graphite low-energy experimental pile), became operational on August 15, 1947, just 20 months after the opening of Harwell. It created the first controlled nuclear chain reaction in Western Europe and was the forerunner of the United Kingdom's nuclear power reactor program.

GLEEP: The Graphite Low Energy Experimental Pile became operational in August 1947 at Harwell. It was the source of the first controlled chain reaction in Western Europe. (Courtesy of AEA Technology–Harwell)

The reactor, which operated reliably for many years, was a tribute to its designers and builders working in difficult postwar conditions. The first experiments in GLEEP investigated the physics of the reactor and demonstrated the inherent stability of graphite-moderated gas-cooled reactors for research and power production. GLEEP was also the first reactor in the United Kingdom to produce radioisotopes for medical and industrial applications.

Because of the extremely stable level of neutrons produced in the reactor core, GLEEP was calibrated as a British Standard neutron source. In this role, the reactor was used for testing and quality control of reactor materials and for calibrating radiation monitors essential for the safe operation of nuclear power plants. The most recent application of the reactor was activation analysis of bore-hole rock samples as an aid to the location and assessment of oil reserves.

The first core consisted of a mixture of natural uranium rods and uranium dioxide cartridges, made necessary because of the shortage of uranium metal at that time. In 1960, the original fuel was replaced by all-metal fuel in aluminum cans, and the final core consisted of 682 channels loaded with 30.7 tonnes of natural uranium.

The design power of GLEEP was 100 kW(t), though a stable power of 700 kW(t) was achieved during experiments proving the negative temperature coefficient of the pile. Subsequently, the reactor spent most of its operational life at 3 kW(t). GLEEP was shutdown in 1990 after 43 years of operation.[3]

[3]"Harwell Shuts Down GLEEP—Britian's Oldest Reactor," *Atom*, No. 407 (October 1990).

Two plutonium production piles were put on line in 1950 and 1951. These reactors used air cooling, vented to the atmosphere through 400-ft stacks. They came to international attention in 1957 when, during a routine shutdown, the Windscale Pile 1 caught fire. Some of the radioactive material released by the burning graphite passed through ventilation filters into the English countryside.

The idea of using a steam boiler to generate electricity in conjunction with a gas-cooled graphite-moderated reactor evolved as early as 1947. Following research at Harwell, the Springfields laboratory developed a break-through magnesium alloy cladding, called Magnox, for the natural uranium rods. The magnesium cladding made possible higher tem-

The Windscale piles: These graphite-moderated, air-cooled production reactors went critical in 1950–51. (Courtesy of British Nuclear Fuels plc)

peratures in the thermal cycle. Christopher Hinton then proposed building the PIPPA (pile for producing plutonium and power) reactor. Four PIPPA reactors were built at Calder Hall, and later, four additional reactors of the same design were built at Chapelcross. The first Calder Hall reactor was opened on October 17, 1956.[4]

[4]"The Life and Times of Lord Hinton of Bankside," *Atom*, No. 414 (June 1991).

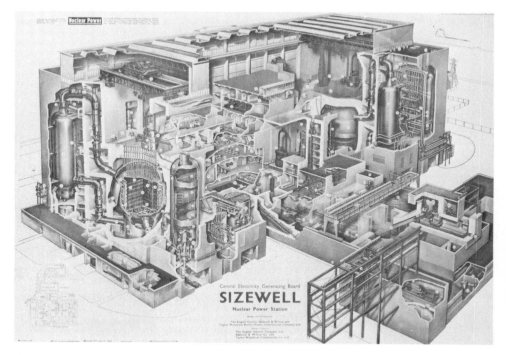

Sizewell A Nuclear Power Station. (Courtesy of Nuclear Electric)

Calder Hall Startup

Her Majesty Queen Elizabeth II said, on the occasion of the opening of the Calder Hall Nuclear Power Station[5]:

...Future generations will judge us, above all else, by the way in which we use these limitless opportunities which Providence has given us and to which we have unlocked the door. They offer us, as we have heard today, a vital and timely addition to the industrial resources of our nation and to our material welfare. But, above all, we have something new to offer to the peoples of the undeveloped and less fortunate areas of the world, who will continue to look to us for assistance and example as they have done in the past.

That, to me, is the real importance of today's ceremony. For centuries past visionary ideals and practical methods which have gone from our shores have opened up new ways of thought and modes of life for people in all parts of the world. It may well prove to have been among the greatest of our contributions to human welfare that we led the way in demonstrating the peaceful uses of a new source of power....

[5]R. F. Pocock, *Nuclear Power: Its Development in the United Kingdom,* The Institution of Nuclear Engineers (1977).

Sizewell A station: These 30-ft-long charge chutes connected the pile cap through the reactor vessel standpipes to the charge pans on top of the graphite moderator for refueling. Because of the large number of fuel channels (about 4000 per reactor), with seven individual elements stacked in each channel, the Magnox stations employed on-load refueling. (Courtesy of NNC Limited)

The Sizewell A Magnox station (2 × 290-MW(e)) refueling machine is moved around the pile cap by crane and was used on either reactor. Sizewell A was the first British nuclear station to incorporate both reactors in a single building. (Courtesy of Nuclear Electric)

Nine Magnox power stations, each consisting of two reactors, were built following Calder Hall and Chapelcross. Construction of the first two, Berkeley and Bradwell, began in 1956, followed by Hunterston, Trawsfynydd, Dungeness, Sizewell A, Hinkley Point A, and Oldbury. The last, Wylfa, was commissioned in 1971 to bring the nine stations to a total capacity of 5000 MW(e). The nine Magnox stations, each one of increasing power, were built by five industrial consortia (four by the end of the series). Consequently, the economic benefits of a standard design were never realized.

Lord Hinton Reflects

Lord Christopher Hinton was to write, late in life[6]:

> ...When we started in 1946 the Americans had a lead of four years on us and those were years in which they had an overriding priority and first call on the services and resources of (a long list) of the great American Corporations. We started four wartime years behind them; after only ten years we had a lead of at least two years. It took only another seven years to throw that lead away....

[6]"The Life and Times of Lord Hinton of Bankside," *Atom*, No. 414 (June 1991).

The natural successor to the Magnox station was an improved design, using slightly enriched oxide fuel with stainless steel cladding and, for more efficiency, operating at a higher gas temperature of approximately 650°C versus 400°C for the Magnox reactors. The prototype Advanced Gas-cooled Reactor (AGR) started operation at Windscale in 1962. The first station, Dungeness B, was only a qualified success, due partly to the problems of scale-

Windscale advanced gas-cooled reactor. This 30-MW(e) reactor was the forerunner of the final U.K. gas-cooled reactor series, the AGRs. It went critical in August 1962 and now after final shutdown is a test bed for decommissioning techniques. (Courtesy of AEA Technology–Harwell)

up from 30 to 600 MW(e), but designs improved with Hinkley Point B and Hunterston B and with Heysham I and Hartlepool. The Hinkley Point B/

Hunterston B design evolved into the fourth and final AGR design, constructed at Heysham II and Torness. These stations, which were ordered in 1978 and commissioned in 1988–89, hold the record for the "fastest work-up to full power" of any reactor in the world.[7]

The third phase of the U.K. thermal reactor development program was the high-temperature gas-cooled reactor, intended to be the successor to the AGRs. The British HTGR used enriched uranium and thorium in graphite cladding, cooled by pressurized helium at a maximum temperature of 750°C, a concept similar to that used in the Peach Bottom demonstration plant in the United States. "Dragon," built at Winfrith Heath with 40% of the funding provided by the European Nuclear Energy Agency, started operation in 1964. Research on this international cooperative reactor project concluded in 1974.

Construction of the graphite moderator for the Magnox Hinkley Point A station (2 × 250 MW(e)). There are about 2000 tonnes of graphite in each reactor. (Courtesy of NNC Limited)

As insurance against possible problems with the AGR reactor development, the Strath Committee on the Reactor Program recommended in 1956, "The best possible alternative system for a commercial nuclear power station in the late 1960s may well be a heavy-water-

---

[7]British Nuclear Forum, "The UK Nuclear Power Program—1945 to 1975," *Atom,* No. 414 (June 1991).

Moving a boiler (steam generator) into position at the Hinkley Point A station. The use of a goliath crane, which bestrode the fabrication area and the reactor buildings, was typical of construction techniques during the British Magnox reactor program. (Courtesy of NNC Limited)

Steam Generating Heavy Water Reactor, Winfrith Heath. The charge face of the SGHWR during construction in 1968. The SGHWR was a heavy-water-moderated, light-water-cooled direct cycle plant of 100-MW(e) designed capacity. (Courtesy of AEA Technology–Reactor Services, Risley)

moderated reactor.... The reactor does not necessarily require a containment vessel capable of withstanding a high pressure.... It may also be suitable for a plutonium recycle fuel scheme in which the fuel feed is natural uranium."[8] The Steam Generating Heavy Water Reactor (SGHWR) was the result of this

[8]R. F. Pocock, *Nuclear Power: Its Development in the United Kingdom,* The Institution of Nuclear Engineers (1977).

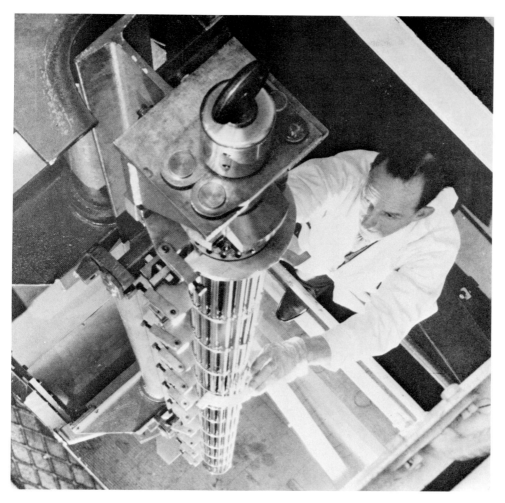

SGHWR: Inspecting one of the 12-foot-long fuel elements. (AEA Technology–Reactor Services, Risley)

challenge. SGHWR was operated from initial attainment of its full power output of 100 MW(e) in 1968 until 1990. Successful experiments on fuel performance and heat transfer during the transition from boiling to steam cooling (dry out) were performed while routinely exporting some 90% of generated power to the grid system. The SGHWR was of pressure-tube design that used a heavy water moderator at low temperature and boiling water at high pressure to provide steam to the turbogenerator.

Fuel element carriers being fitted for the Prototype Fast Reactor designed at the Stockport works of Fairey Engineering Ltd. (Courtesy of AEA Technology–Reactor Services, Risley)

PFR, the 250-MW(e) LMFBR built at Dounreay, Scotland, during construction. It went critical in March 1974 and entered commercial operation in August 1976. (Courtesy of AEA Technology–Reactor Services, Risley)

The SGHWR was favored in the mid-1970s as the future power source in the United Kingdom, but because of the vast experience with pressurized water reactors in the United States and elsewhere, the PWR was chosen for future development. The first U.K. PWR is being constructed at Sizewell B with the plan to build the second at Hinkley Point C.

ZENITH II, this zero-energy reactor was designed for the third phase of the UKAEA's GCR program—the high-temperature gas-cooled reactor. This experimental physics reactor, which started in 1971–72, was about 6 m high, 6 m in diameter including reflectors, and used about 5 tons of fuel. (Courtesy of AEA Technology–Reactor Services, Risley)

Sizewell B station. This 1188-MW(e) PWR marks the beginning of the U.K. PWR program and the demise of the GCR series. (Courtesy of Nuclear Electric)

Windscale AGR pilecap showing the refueling machine. (Courtesy of AEA Technology–
Reactor Services, Risley)

As in the United States, the fast reactor was recognized in the earliest years
for its potential for maximum uranium utilization. Pioneering experiments
were done at Harwell with the critical assemblies ZEPHYR (1954) and ZEUS
(1959). These experiments helped in the design of the 60-MW(t) metallic-

Heysham II AGR. This 2 × 620-MW(e) station is one of the two final AGR orders. Consider the developments in refueling machine design as the GCRs developed. (Courtesy of Nuclear Electric)

fueled Dounreay Fast Reactor, which went critical in 1959. Development proceeded with the construction of a 250-MW(e) prototype fast reactor (PFR), which uses Pu-U oxide ceramic fuel. The PFR, first taken critical in 1974, is scheduled to operate until 1994. In 1989, design work for a follow-on 1200-MW(e) commercial size plant to follow PFR was merged into the European collaboration to design the European Fast Reactor.

France⁹

France wasted no time in resuming nuclear research and development once peace was restored after World War II. Proud of the role Joliot-Curie and other French scientists had played in the discovery of fission, and having suffered years of German occupation during the war, France was motivated to become

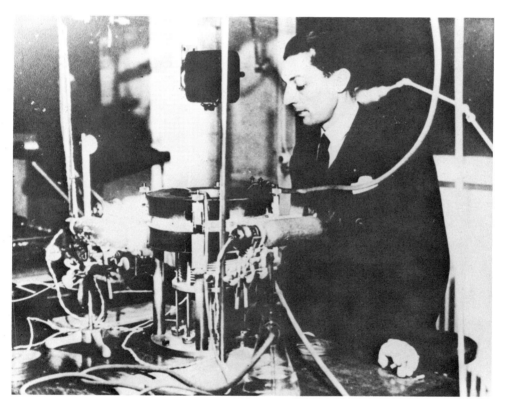

Frédéric Joliot-Curie, the first high commissioner for atomic energy in 1946. (Courtesy of Electricité de France)

a nuclear power—both in military and peaceful applications. That motivation has been translated into what is arguably the world's greatest nuclear electric generating program. With approximately 75% of its electricity today being generated by nuclear power plants, France has become a leading international

---

⁹This section draws extensively from B. Goldschmidt, *The Atomic Complex*, American Nuclear Society, La Grange Park, IL (1982).

ZOE, the first French atomic reactor, located at Fontenay-aux-Roses. It started up December 15, 1948. (Courtesy of Electricité de France)

competitor in the nuclear marketplace. Along the way, French scientists and engineers have demonstrated leadership in the development of gas, pressurized water, and liquid-metal-cooled reactors, as well as fuel cycle technologies.

The Commissariat à l'Energie Atomique (CEA) was founded in 1945 and immediately began basic research. The first French reactor, ZOE, went critical in 1947. Built at Fort Chatillon in the Paris suburbs, ZOE was the first of a series of heavy water test reactors built by the CEA.

In 1952, following a favorable vote by the French Parliament on Felix Gaillard's proposal for a five-year national nuclear plan, the CEA developed an industrial program. Prospecting in the Limousin mountains of France was well along, indicating that an annual production of some hundreds of tonnes of uranium could be expected by 1957. The ready availability of uranium made it possible to consider construction of several plutonium-producing reactors. CEA decided to build two large reactors, moderated by graphite, at a new site at Marcoule near Avignon. Graphite was chosen because French industry was able to produce it in very pure form, but could not yet separate heavy water. The two reactors, from which no recovery of energy was initially planned, were intended to produce plutonium. Extracting the plutonium would require a reprocessing plant, which was to be built on the same site so as to provide a complete production capability.

Military considerations were never far from the minds of those responsible for the five-year plan. However, the plan's explanatory notes mentioned that France had always been short of coal in sufficient quantities and particularly

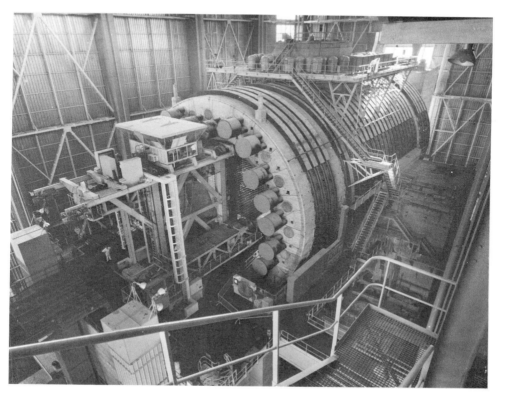

The G2 reactor at Marcoule first generated power in 1959. The 40-MW(e) reactor introduced the concepts of on-load refueling and the prestressed concrete pressure vessel, although it only enclosed the core. (Courtesy of Commissariat à l'Energie Atomique)

in appropriate qualities, had fallen behind in the highly competitive race for oil, and had limited hydroelectric generation capacity. It was therefore essential for France to possess enough plutonium for its first ventures—power stations and propulsion systems—in utilizing the new form of energy.

During 1952, a second heavy water research reactor with a power of 2 MW(t) came into use at the Saclay center. Its fuel rods of uranium metal were cooled by compressed carbon dioxide, the first use of this method anywhere. The CO_2 cooling process was so successful that a proposal was made that the projected graphite reactors of the five-year plan be modified in order to include provision for the experimental production of electricity. Since the end of 1952, it had been intended that the first reactor would be cooled by air at atmospheric pressure, as were those at Windscale, but that the second would use carbon dioxide under pressure. Toward the end of 1953 the decision was made to add a small electricity production unit to both reactors. France thus took the road toward dual-purpose reactor prototypes. In March 1955, the characteristics of the second French plutonium-producing reactor, G2, were finalized. Like the Calder Hall units in the United Kingdom, G2 was to be a natural uranium, graphite-moderated reactor, cooled by gas under pressure.

As had been the case in the United States and the United Kingdom, the transition to the industrial stage was successfully accomplished with the help of a specialist engineer from a leading branch of industry—in France's case, the oil industry. Pierre Taranger, the first industrial director of the CEA, provided the essential working liaison between the laboratories and industry and made each of them understand the problems and needs of the other. Taranger was also responsible for the choice of prestressed concrete for the G2 reactor pressure vessel, in preference to a steel vessel. This successful innovation was subsequently widely adopted.

In 1955, the two top men in the CEA, Pierre Guillaumat and Francis Perrin, believed that the CEA had reached the stage where the first steps should be undertaken in concert with the national utility, Electricité de France (EDF), toward launching a French program for civilian nuclear power. The Production d'Electricité d'Origine Nucléaire (PEON) Commission was established with representatives from EDF, the CEA, and industry. By the summer of 1955, the PEON Commission had approved a program to develop a series of prototype power stations, starting with a 70-MW(e) plant to be known as EDF1. All units in the series would be based on the technology of the Marcoule reactors, each being more powerful than its predecessor. An interval of 18 months was planned between the construction of each plant, in the hope that a given reactor could then benefit from previous experience acquired in construction and operation. In this way, it was foreseen that by 1965 generating capacity would reach at least 800 MW(e). In presenting this program, EDF Director Pierre Ailleret declared that "there can be no hesitation over the type of reactor to adopt for France's first atomic power stations: we can only consider graphite reactors of the type built at Marcoule."[10]

In 1955, construction of an enriched uranium reactor was not a viable option in France. French research into isotopic separation of uranium by gaseous diffusion was still in its infancy and the American government had not yet authorized the export of U-235 other than for research reactors. The long-term French planning anticipated three stages: (1) power plants using natural uranium, (2) plants using fuel enriched with plutonium produced in the first plants, and (3) plutonium-fueled breeder reactors.

The minimum objective of 800-MW(e) installed nuclear capacity in EDF plants was not achieved until early 1969, four years behind schedule. Only EDF1 was in operation in 1964, with construction of EDF2 just completed. Both plants were sited on the Loire River near Chinon.

---

[10]B. Goldschmidt, *The Atomic Complex*, American Nuclear Society, La Grange Park, IL (1982).

The Chinon site showing the first three EDF gas-cooled reactors, EDF 1, 2, and 3. The unit sizes increased from 70 to 210 and 480 MW(e). These plants have all been shut down and four 900-MW(e) PWRs added to the site. (Courtesy of Electricité de France)

It was decided early in 1956 to place overall responsibility for EDF1 in the hands of Electricité de France. CEA was to prepare the basic plans for the project, design and manufacture the specifically nuclear items, and supply the graphite and fuel. For subsequent power stations, the CEA's role was more limited. By 1958, CEA's contribution to EDF3 was reduced to fuel supply, technical data, and testing.

The basic design for EDF1 was a reactor with horizontal fuel and cooling channels (as in the G2 pile whose construction had just begun) contained within a prestressed concrete pressure vessel. However EDF, in its capacity as industrial architect for this and subsequent plants, was seeking wider technological experience. Preferring the design adopted by the British, EDF decided in favor of vertical channels, a choice that proved satisfactory and was maintained for the later power stations. Also like the British, EDF chose a steel pressure vessel, partly because the design pressure of the coolant gas was higher than in G2, but also in consideration of problems being experienced with passing conduit pipes through prestressed concrete.

Early in 1959, a crack developed in the EDF1 pressure vessel as it was being assembled, drawing attention to the difficulty of welding thick steel plates in the large sizes required. Construction problems took a long time to overcome, delaying the completion of both EDF1 and EDF2 by about three years. Meanwhile, the prestressed concrete vessels, which were quickly built for G2 and G3, proved highly satisfactory from the moment of first operation. In 1960, EDF changed to concrete vessels for the 400-MW(e) EDF3 and subsequent units. A year later the British made the same type of change. The reactor and

The 310-MW(e) SENA Chooz A nuclear plant was a joint French-Belgian project. The nuclear part of the plant was built in the hillside with the electrical plant aboveground. It generated from 1967 to 1991. Two plants of the new 1400-MW(e) series are currently being built at the site. (Courtesy of Electricité de France)

heat exchangers in EDF4 comprised a combined unit inside the reinforced concrete containment.

In 1963, the startup and good performance of the land-based prototype French submarine engine demonstrated the CEA engineers' command of PWR technology. At the same time, EDF was acquiring PWR technology by building, as a joint French-Belgian project, a Westinghouse-type PWR power station at Chooz, near the Belgian border. The 310-MW(e) Chooz plant was commissioned in 1966.

There were other nuclear technology developments in France about the same time. EL4, a prototype CEA-designed heavy-water-moderated, natural uranium reactor, cooled by pressurized carbon dioxide, was built by EDF and the CEA in the Monts d'Arree in Brittany. The plant became operational in 1967. An experimental sodium-cooled fast neutron reactor, Rapsodie, was completed in 1965 at the CEA's Cadarache research center. To complete the fuel cycle, the French program was also actively developing capabilities for uranium enrichment, fuel reprocessing, and waste storage and disposal.[11,12]

---

[11]B. Goldschmidt, *The Atomic Complex*, American Nuclear Society, La Grange Park, IL (1982).
[12]Jacques Leclercq, *The Nuclear Age*, Sodel (1986).

Rapsodie: This was the 40-MW(t) test reactor for the French LMFBR program. It operated from 1967 to 1983 and provided the basis for the Phénix reactor. (Courtesy of Commissariat à l'Energie Atomique)

GCR fuel reprocessing capability was available at Marcoule from 1958. The Pierrelatte uranium enrichment plant began operation in 1967.

In 1965, EDF decided to build two new nuclear power stations for entry into service in 1971. One was essentially identical to EDF4 and was built on the same site at Saint-Laurent-des-Eaux on the Loire River. The second new station, with a 540-MW(e) capacity, was built at Bugey, near Lyon, and used the improved annular form of fuel with both external and internal cladding and cooling. This new fuel was intended to enable a higher power density to

The Bugey site includes the last French GCR plant (540-MW(e)), which was commissioned in 1972, and four 900-MW(e) PWRs, which came on line during the period 1979–83. (Courtesy of Electricité de France)

be obtained by raising the coolant pressure; it was hoped that this improvement could eventually lead to a new design for a power reactor producing up to 1000 MW(e).

But other developments intervened. The Bugey and Saint-Laurent-des-Eaux GCR stations, along with a similar plant at Vandellos in Spain, were the last of their type to be built. They were brought into service in 1971 and 1972. For several years the choice of reactor type for the next series of plants was debated between the CEA and EDF. The performance of the various existing plants influenced the debate, as did the frenzy of nuclear orders in the United States. However, the final choice of the LWR was justified neither by a better performance of the prototypes (the commissioning of the first French-Belgian PWR was followed by a two-year shutdown) nor by any important economic superiority, but by the advantage of benefiting from operational experience that was to reach worldwide proportions.

As early as 1970, EDF ordered its first PWR power station, with a generating capacity of 900 MW(e), from the Schneider Group. Their subsidiary, Framatome, held the Westinghouse license. At the end of that year, the decision was made to build more of these plants over five years to a total capacity of 8000 MW(e)

This advanced annular fuel element was designed for the Bugey 1 plant and was an attempt to improve GCR economics by increasing the reactor power density. (Courtesy of Commissariat à l'Energie Atomique)

Two of them were ordered in late 1971 from the same supplier, despite considerable pressure in favor of the BWR. In 1972, Framatome was reorganized, giving Westinghouse a 45% holding and Creusot-Loire 55%.

Early in 1973, the French nuclear program was accelerated as rising oil prices gave warning of oncoming trouble. For France, nuclear energy became the only possible option. The prime minister immediately decided to increase the rate of ordering plants to between five and six 900-MW(e) units per year. French industry had consolidated into a centralized structure with well-defined roles for the major organizations, clearing the way for France's eventual entry into international nuclear competition. EDF was given sole

Cruas: This 4 × 880-MW(e) station entered commercial operations in 1984–85. (Courtesy of Electricité de France)

responsibility as architect-engineer for French plants; Framatome became the reactor supplier; Alsthom was responsible for turbine-generators; and Cogema was given responsibility for complete fuel cycle services.

In late 1973, EDF announced an all-nuclear policy. It would build no more fuel oil or coal-burning power stations, but rather would increase its nuclear generating capacity at an annual rate of some 5000 MW(e). Total installed nuclear capacity at the time was some 2000 MW(e). With each nuclear plant then taking about six years to build, the target date of 1985 for producing more than 60% of all French electricity from uranium was ambitious. France achieved this goal on schedule, and today generates approximately 75% of its electricity by nuclear power. The standard 900-MW(e) series of PWRs was replaced in the 1980s by an upgraded 1300-MW(e) design. During the 1990s, 1400-MW(e) PWRs will go on line in France.

The same year that EDF announced its all-nuclear policy, the 250-MW(e) Phénix prototype breeder reactor was brought into operation at Marcoule. Phénix was built under the direction of Georges Vendryes, the physicist who was the inspiration behind the French liquid-metal reactor program. Following the successful commissioning and startup of Phénix, EDF began preparing for the construction of a "pre-commercial prototype" at a site between Lyon and Geneva. The 1200-MW(e) Super Phénix plant was built in association with a German electric utility, RWE, and the nationalized Italian utility, ENEL.

Belleville: This 2 × 1300-MW(e) station entered service in 1988–89. (Courtesy of Electricité de France)

Super Phénix was connected to the grid in January 1986, but has suffered repeated operational difficulties in recent years. The proposed Super Phénix II plant has now been merged with the European Fast Reactor program.

Soviet Union (USSR)[*][13]

Despite the opening of communications during the past six years, even with accelerated exchange of information on the safety of Soviet-built reactors in the past year, the history of the Soviet nuclear program is still not thoroughly understood in the West. Not enough is known to acknowledge the responsible individuals, at least not in balance with the Western programs described earlier. This is unfortunate, because the Soviet nuclear program can boast of many technical achievements, including development of several types of reactors as well as enrichment and reprocessing technologies. The significance of these accomplishments is enhanced by the fact that they were largely made while the USSR was undergoing major reconstruction following World War II.

In reactor development, the Soviets became world leaders in LMR technology in the early 1970s, rivaled only by accomplishments in the French pro-

---

[*] Since these achievements were accomplished before the establishment of the Commonwealth of Independent States, they will be acknowledged as accomplishments of the Soviet Union.

[13] This section draws extensively from B. Goldschmidt, *The Atomic Complex*, American Nuclear Society, La Grange Park, IL (1982).

gram. PWRs were developed, deployed, and even exported to a limited extent. The USSR was the only country that developed water-cooled, graphite-moderated reactors for widespread domestic deployment. The USSR was also the only country that succeeded in routinely using reactors to power space satellites, and it had the only commercial fleet of nuclear-powered ships. Looking to the future, the Soviets have been leaders in fusion technology since the early 1950s. On the military side, the rapid development of nuclear explosives that established the Soviet Union as a nuclear superpower is well known. However, the Soviet Union's application of nuclear explosives to such civilian projects as oil exploration and construction excavation is known to relatively few westerners. The Soviets also developed the fastest nuclear submarines.

The impressive military and civilian Soviet achievements indicate the high level of priority accorded to nuclear development. As communications have opened up with the West, however, it is not the successes that have been the focus of attention, but rather the failures. Perhaps it was the urgency to succeed that led to a tragic underestimation of the safety requirements for some phases of the Soviet nuclear development program.[14] Besides the Chernobyl accident, there have been reactor accidents on submarines and an icebreaker, a disastrous explosion in a radioactive waste tank near Kyshtym, Russia, and a reactor-powered satellite that crashed harmlessly in northern Canada. Today the key focus of the nuclear programs in the former Soviet republics is in making safety improvements.

Soviet scientists were clearly aware of the uranium question by the spring of 1940. A special committee on the subject was set up under the auspices of the Soviet Union's Academy of Sciences, and funds, although very scarce, were allocated for uranium prospecting. From reports prepared in 1941 at the Soviet academy, it was clear that the very far-reaching consequences of the discovery of fission were fully appreciated by a number of Soviet physicists, who were calling on their government to launch immediate studies of the subject in order to avoid being overtaken by other countries.

In the fall of 1942, the physicist Igor Kurchatov was asked to investigate the possibility of military applications, but

> From reports prepared in 1941 at the Soviet academy, it was clear that the very far-reaching consequences of the discovery of fission were fully appreciated by a number of Soviet physicists...

---

[14]Edith M. Lederer and Sergel Shargorodsky, "The Soviet Nuclear Legacy," Associated Press Report (July 1992).

his work was impeded by the German invasion of the Soviet Union, which caused the Soviet specialist teams to be dispersed and assigned to more urgent research. Work in the nuclear physics laboratories did not resume until 1943, after the Battle of Stalingrad, and even then the program remained on a rather small scale until the end of hostilities.

A draft agreement had been worked out early in 1943 for a complete collaboration between British and Soviet scientists engaged in military research. President Roosevelt opposed the scheme, which was therefore abandoned. As a result, there was no real wartime collaboration between Anglo-American and Soviet scientific research in any domain.

Nevertheless, as early as 1944, the Soviets attacked the problems of producing pure uranium and

Igor Kurchatov: First director of the Soviet Union's Atomic Energy Institute of the Academy of Sciences, which now bears his name. (Courtesy of Ex-Soviet Nuclear Society)

graphite. The American success in 1945 resulted in the highest priority being given to plutonium production, weapons studies, and the construction of a test site. The first Soviet reactor achieved criticality almost four years to the day after Fermi's CP-1, which it closely resembled. This four-year gap never widened. Construction of plutonium-producing reactors, a plutonium extraction plant, and the final development of a military nuclear capability were all achieved at the same remarkable pace as the corresponding American accomplishments.

The gaseous diffusion process for isotopic separation of U-235 was developed in parallel with the plutonium work. Starting late in 1949, the Soviets began design studies for the construction of their first atomic power station and several experimental reactors, all using enriched uranium. This indicates that the isotopic separation plant must have been available some two to three years after the first industrial production of plutonium.

Soviet Nuclear Institutions

The history of nuclear energy in the USSR is tightly connected with the history of the leading nuclear science institutions, which determined the course of peaceful uses of nuclear energy as well as military applications in the country. These institutions, which have received worldwide recognition, include:

- The Radium Institute in Leningrad, now St. Petersburg, developed the technology for plutonium separation from irradiated uranium and was a founder of theoretical and practical dosimetry.

- The Physico-Technical Institute trained the first generation of Soviet nuclear scientists, who later founded the network of Soviet nuclear research centers and laboratories.

- The Lebedev Institute of Physics of the Russian Academy of Science (FIAN) conducts studies on nuclear physics, gamma and x rays, space radiation, and theoretical aspects of nuclear particle acceleration. It was at the Lebedev Institute that Cherenkov radiation was discovered.

- The Khar'kov Physico-Technical Institute of the Ukrainian Academy of Sciences is one of the leading centers of nuclear science and has the unique thermonuclear fusion installations "Sirius" and "Uragan." Cesium plasma research is conducted on the largest stellarator-type experimental installation, "Uragan," in the former Soviet Union.

After World War II, several other institutions were founded with the prime goal of practical applications of nuclear energy:

- The Kurchatov Institute of Atomic Energy (IAE) in Moscow became the main center of Soviet nuclear science. It was founded in 1943 by Igor Kurchatov, its first director. In a very short time the institute became a large, multidisciplinary center for nuclear and reactor physics research. The institute has unique experimental installations such as the nuclear research reactor called F-1, in which the first European nuclear chain reaction was conducted on December 25, 1946, and a 40-MW high-flux research reactor called MR that has been in operation since 1963. Among other research reactors are a 2.5-MW VVR-2 reactor, a 5-MW IRT-M reactor, a reactor with organic heat-transfer media (OR-100), and other experimental installations. The first and the best thermonuclear experimental installations of a Tokamak-type were created in the institute. Fundamental studies of plasma properties are conducted on the Tokamak-15 installation.

Graphite stack of research reactor F-1, the first European nuclear reactor, which was started in December 1946 at the Kurchatov Institute of Atomic Energy. (Courtesy of Ex-Soviet Nuclear Society)

- The Institute of Physics and Power Engineering (FEI) is located 100 km from Moscow in the city of Obninsk. A small 5-MW(e) plant, APS-1, was started up in 1954. The reactor has a graphite moderator and boiling light water cooling of low-enrichment fuel in pressure tubes. In 1956 the fast reactor BR-2 began operation. In 1958 BR-2 was replaced by a sodium-cooled fast reactor named BR-5 [5-MW(t)]. In the 1970s, reactor BR-5 was upgraded and renamed BR-10 [10-MW(t)]. The institute has 30 critical assemblies and nuclear reactors. A special cyclotron accelerator was constructed here that allows production of a variety of radioactive isotopes that cannot be obtained from other reactors. The largest thermo-physics and hydrodynamics research laboratory in the country is located in the institute.

- The Research Institute of Atomic Reactors (NIIAR) is the biggest materials science research center in the Soviet Union and one of the largest in the world. It is located in Dimitrovgrad and includes many materials science research reactors and experimental power reactors, including BOR-60 (started up in 1969), VI-50 (1965), and AST-1 (1979).

In 1954, Obninsk APS-1 was the first reactor to generate appreciable electric power, 5 MW(e), for a sustained period. (Courtesy of Ex-Soviet Nuclear Society)

APS-1, the 5-MW(e) power plant commissioned at Obninsk in 1954, became the world's first nuclear electric generating station. As a result of the performance of APS-1, Soviet scientists were able to attend the 1955 Atoms for Peace conference as champions of the peaceful application of nuclear energy. The Obninsk APS-1 reactor was the precursor of the indigenous graphite-moderated boiling-water-cooled reactor (LWGR), known as RBMK. The RBMK series began with Beloyarsk 1 [102-MW(e)] and Beloyarsk 2 [200-MW(e)] commissioned in 1964 and 1967, respectively, and culminated in the 2 × 1500-MW(e) Ignalina plant using RBMK reactors in Lithuania. This series included the Chernobyl plant in the Ukraine.

The USSR built the only significant fleet of nonmilitary nuclear-powered ships, most of which are icebreakers. PWR technology was used for both icebreaker and submarine fleets. Based on this background, the technology was developed for the VVER power stations. The VVER reactor series [in plant sizes of about 440 MW(e)] was exported to Finland and eastern European countries. VVERs of 1000-MW(e) size were later developed and deployed in Soviet power stations.

Novovoronezh Unit V: This VVER-1000 reactor entered operation in 1980. The four other reactors were a VVER-210, a VVER-365, and two VVER-440-230s. The first unit started operation in 1964. (Courtesy of Ex-Soviet Nuclear Society)

The Soviet Union was the only country to build a significant number of civilian nuclear ships, mainly icebreakers. This picture is of the icebreaker Lenin. (Courtesy of Ex-Soviet Nuclear Society)

(a)

Shevchenko BN350: Situated on the shore of the Caspian Sea the plant generates 135 MW(e) and provides steam for an associated desalination plant: (a) View of the interior of the reactor hall, and (b) view of the only nuclear-heated desalination unit in the world. (Courtesy of Ex-Soviet Nuclear Society)

(b)

Civilian Nuclear-Powered Ships in the Former Soviet Republics

Ship Type*	Name	Number of Reactors	Start-up Year	Shaft Horsepower**
Icebreaker	Lenin	3	1959	22,000
Icebreaker	Arktika	2	1975	27,000
Icebreaker	Sibir	2	1978	27,000
Icebreaker	Rossiya	2	1985	27,000
Freighter	Sevmorput	1	1988	30,000
Icebreaker	Taimyr	1	1990	37,000
Transport barge	Arkhangelsk	2	1983	not available

*All these ships operate in the Artic Ocean out of the port of Murmansk.
**Power is given for each reactor aboard the ship.

The third main reactor type developed in the Soviet Union was the liquid-metal-cooled fast breeder reactor. The Obninsk research reactor, BR5/10, has operated since 1958. In 1969, the first Soviet breeder for the generation of electricity went critical. Designated BOR-60, this small LMR has a power level of 60 MW(t) and 12 MW(e). The next step in LMR development was the BN 350, which entered commercial operation at Shevchenko in 1973 and provides steam to the associated desalination plant.[15] BN 600, the next LMR in the series, started up in 1980 at Beloyarsk. Designs have been produced for 800- and 1600-MW(e) reactors, but a construction project for an 800-MW(e) plant at Beloyarsk has been delayed.

International Technology Transfer[16]

Although the transfer of nuclear technology began in earnest after the 1955 Geneva Atoms for Peace conference, two reactors built earlier involved bilateral cooperation by countries not directly involved in the war effort. Shortly after the war, the Norwegian government, proud of its national production of heavy water, initiated construction of a low-power, heavy water research reactor on the assumption that a domestic supply of uranium would be found. By 1950, the reactor construction was well along, but the uranium search had been disappointing, and Norway turned to its European neighbors for help. Gunnar Randers, the physicist in charge of the project, was unable to acquire the needed uranium from the European countries that had involvement in the wartime nuclear enterprises, even in exchange for heavy water.

[15]Jacques Leclercq, *The Nuclear Age,* Sodel (1986).
[16]This section draws extensively from B. Goldschmidt, *The Atomic Complex,* American Nuclear Society, La Grange Park, IL (1982).

However, Randers was able to conclude an agreement with the Netherlands, which had a hidden uranium stock available from 1939. The Dutch-Norwegian reactor was completed in 1951 at the Kjeller Center, near Oslo. Kjeller became the first nuclear establishment to open its doors to scientists and technicians from other countries.

In 1954, a similar research reactor was built near Stockholm by a joint French-Swedish collaboration. The design and building of this reactor was largely due to the work of the Swedish physicist Sigvard Eklund, who later became head of the International Atomic Energy Agency (IAEA).

In 1953, the world's first international atomic conference was held in Oslo at the instigation of Randers. The conference, a great success, led to the formation of the European Atomic Energy Society, which eventually was able to start breaking down the psychological barriers in place after 15 years of secrecy. Continental Western Europe was trying to accelerate its nuclear development just as the McMahon Act was being amended in the United States to allow international transfer of nuclear materials and related data for civilian applications.

In practice, only declassified information, i.e., information released from secret classification and subsequently published, was allowed to be distributed. Hence, a considerable amount of information had to be declassified for the United Nations Conference on the Peaceful Uses of Atomic Energy. The UN conference, proposed by the United States and approved by the UN General Assembly, was not only the largest international scientific meeting ever held, but was also a noteworthy political event. The conference took place in August 1955 in Geneva under the presidency of Homi J. Bhabha, chairman of the Indian Atomic Energy Commission. In his opening address, Bhabha emphasized the benefits that nuclear electricity production could bring, both to industrialized countries and to the underdeveloped areas of the world. In his words, there was no energy more expensive than no energy. He pointed out that 80% of India's energy at that time was still obtained by burning cow dung, which globally had only recently been replaced by oil as the second most used fuel after coal. In the same speech, looking to the more distant future, Bhabha mentioned the possible peaceful application of fusion.

The remarkably successful Geneva conference confirmed the thaw in international nuclear relations. About 1500 delegates from around the world met and presented more than 1000 papers, abolishing the secrecy that until then had shrouded many areas of nuclear research. But there were exceptions. Nothing was disclosed about national uranium resources and production, nor anything beyond the already well-known basic principles for separating uranium isotopes. On the other hand, technical data relevant to all other stages of the nuclear fuel cycle were made freely available. Papers disclosed methods for chemically processing uranium ore, as well as for preparation of nuclear-grade uranium oxide and uranium metal (i.e., purified to a very high degree from contamination by neutron-absorbing substances). Papers described the preparation of moderating media—heavy water and high purity graphite—and special metals, such as pure magnesium and zirconium used for cladding uranium fuel rods.

The development of all this specialized industrial chemistry related to nuclear energy had been among the greatest tasks of the previous years. Publication of the data represented an invaluable savings in time and money for the nations starting civilian nuclear development programs. However, the problems of irradiated materials behavior were recognized as major factors governing the commercial viability of nuclear-generated electricity, and the secrecy of industrial competitiveness replaced the secrecy of state security.

Despite all the publicity of future promise, the conference also began to give some idea of the scale and difficulties associated with the new technologies. In fact, production of nuclear electricity was still very much in its infancy; the only civilian power station in operation was the 5-MW(e) plant that the Soviet Union had commissioned in 1954 at Obninsk. Only a few other nuclear plants of similar or higher power were under construction. They were the dual-purpose GCR installations being built in England at Calder Hall and in France at Marcoule, each intended to produce some tens of megawatts electric; and the 60-MW(e) Shippingport PWR plant. However, a great many more reactor prototypes were being designed.

Only six countries took part in the rush to build the first nuclear power stations—the United States, the United Kingdom, France, the Soviet Union, Canada, and Sweden. All other countries were in due course to turn to one or another of these six pioneers for assistance with their first power reactors and subsequent nuclear construction programs. The first exported plants were from the United Kingdom to Italy (Latina) and Japan (Tokai Mura), and from the United States to Italy (Trino Vercellese and Garigliano) and Belgium (BR3–Vulcain).[17] The 1960s saw export orders from Europe and Asia, mainly to U.S. suppliers, but also including Canadian, German, and French vendors. Some companies in these importing countries developed licensee arrangements, which helped to establish domestic vendors that could later compete internationally. Such programs were established early in France, Germany, and Japan. Most modern contracts in all countries now include terms for technology transfer.

Although a significant fraction of the USSR's domestic installed nuclear capacity is water-cooled, graphite-moderated (RBMK) plants, the only type exported was the pressurized light water (VVER) design, similar in type to those exported by U.S. vendors and their former licensees. Apart from those

---

[17]Jacques Leclercq, *The Nuclear Age*, Sodel (1986).

exported to Finland, which admixed some western technology into the plants, Soviet exports were exclusively to Comecon members.

Nuclear safety agencies, as well as the market and the vendors, have become international. A maturing market for nuclear power products has led to international mergers of nuclear vendors, international cooperative ventures, and the opening up of international markets that were formerly closed. International cooperation on a governmental agency level has been demonstrated since the first Geneva conference, e.g., the International Atomic Energy Agency, Euratom, the Organization for Economic Cooperation and Development–Nuclear Energy Agency, and more recently by electric utilities through the World Association of Nuclear Operators.

BIBLIOGRAPHY

———. 1991. *AECL 1991 Annual Review.* Atomic Energy of Canada Limited.

Arnold, Lorna. May 1987. "As It Happened," *Atom*, No. 367.

Benedict, Manson, Thomas H. Pigford, and Hans Wolfgang Levi. 1981. *Nuclear Chemical Engineering.* McGraw-Hill Book Co.

British Nuclear Forum. June 1991. "The UK Nuclear Power Programme 1945 to 1975," *Atom*, No. 414.

———. 1986. *Glossary of Terms in Nuclear Science and Technology.* American Nuclear Society, La Grange Park, IL.

Goldschmidt, B. 1982. *The Atomic Complex.* American Nuclear Society, La Grange Park, IL.

Gowing, Margaret. 1974. *Independence and Deterrence, Britain and Atomic Energy 1945–1952.* Macmillan.

Gowing, Margaret. 1990. *Lord Hinton: Biographical Memoir of Fellows of the Royal Society,* Vol. 36. Royal Society.

———. October 1990. "Harwell Shuts Down GLEEP—Britian's Oldest Reactor," *Atom*, No. 407.

Knief, Ronald Allen. 1981. *Nuclear Energy Technology: Theory and Practice of Commercial Nuclear Power.* Hemisphere Publishing Corp.

Laurence, George C. 1991. "Early Years of Nuclear Energy Research in Canada." Atomic Energy of Canada Limited Research, CRL availability.

Leclercq, Jacques. 1986. *The Nuclear Age.* Sodel.

Lederer, Edith M., and Sergel Shargorodsky. July 1992. "The Soviet Nuclear Legacy." Associated Press Report.

———. June 1991. "The Life and Times of Lord Hinton of Bankside," *Atom,* No. 414.

Pocock, R. F. 1977. *Nuclear Power, Its Development in the United Kingdom.* The Institution of Nuclear Engineers.

———. 1989. *Transactions International Conference on Nuclear Fission: Fifty Years of Progress in Energy Security–Proceedings of the Plenary Sessions.* Washington, DC, October 30–November 4, 1988.

Yankee Atomic Electric Company's 167-MW(e) PWR at Rowe, Massachusetts, which produced power for over 30 years. (Courtesy of Yankee Atomic Electric Company)

Diablo Canyon nuclear power plant composed of 1120- and 1139-MW(e) PWRs at Avila Beach, California. (Courtesy of Pacific Gas and Electric Company)

Palo Verde nuclear generating station, which consists of three 1221-MW(e) PWRs at Wintersburg, Arizona. (Courtesy of Arizona Public Service Company)

Dampierre nuclear power plant with its four 890-MW(e) PWRs in the Loire Valley in France. (Courtesy of Electricité de France)

The six BWR units at the Fukushima Daiichi nuclear power station in Japan as of 1987.
(Courtesy of Tokyo Electric Power Company)

Limerick nuclear generating station's two 1055-MW(e) BWRs at Pottstown, Pennsylvania.
(Courtesy of Philadelphia Electric Company)

Pickering station in Ontario with its eight 515-MW(e) PHWRs. The plant was built over 20 years, the first unit going into commercial service in 1971 and the last in 1986. (Courtesy of AECL–CANDU and Ontario Hydro)

Many aspects of the Canadian nuclear power program are shown. At the left is the 216-MW(e) PHWR Douglas Point plant, which is no longer in service. Also shown are the two Bruce stations, one with four 769-MW(e) PHWRs and the other with four 860-MW(e) PHWRs, and the Bruce heavy water production plant with a capacity of 4 × 720 tonnes per year. (Courtesy of Tom Bochsler/AECL–CANDU and Ontario Hydro)

The first unit of Calder Hall, a 50-MW(e) GCR, was officially opened on October 17, 1956. It was the first nuclear generating station in the West, and it continues operation today along with three additional 50-MW(e) GCRs. Units 3, 2, and 1 are seen from the Calder River. (Courtesy of AEA Technology–Harwell)

The core of the 250-MW(e) Prototype Fast Reactor (PFR) at Dounreay in the United Kingdom. Shown are the neutron shield and reflector rods as a dummy fuel assembly is being lowered into place. (Courtesy of AEA Technology–Harwell and Reactor Services, Risley)

The Russian icebreaker *Sibir*, which started operation in 1978 with its two reactors that are capable of delivering 27,000 shaft horsepower. (Courtesy of Ex-Soviet Nuclear Society)

A bucolic view of Sellafield, the United Kingdom's center for reprocessing in West Cumbria. Shown are two of Calder Hall's cooling towers, the two Windscale air-cooled piles, an AGR, and parts of the reprocessing complex. (Courtesy of British Nuclear Fuels plc)

La Hague reprocessing plant in France. (Courtesy of Cogema)

An *in situ* vitrification process for the remediation of radioactive, hazardous, and mixed wastes. (Courtesy of U.S. Department of Energy)

Interior view of the Joint European Torus, JET. (Courtesy of JET Joint Undertaking)

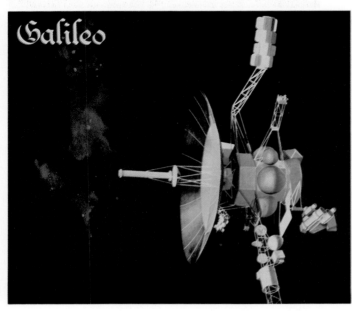

The Galileo spacecraft, powered by a radioisotopic thermoelectric generator for its mission to Jupiter. (Courtesy of U.S. Department of Energy)

Monju, a 280-MW(e) LMFBR under construction at Tsuruga, Japan. (Courtesy of Power Reactor and Nuclear Fuel Development Corporation)

Tokamak Fusion Test Reactor at Princeton University. (Courtesy of U.S. Department of Energy)

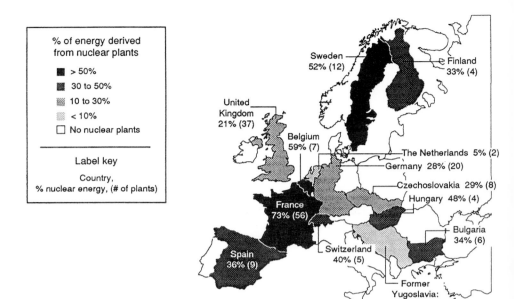

% of energy derived
from nuclear plants

■ > 50%
▨ 30 to 50%
▦ 10 to 30%
░ < 10%
☐ No nuclear plants

Label key

Country,
% nuclear energy, (# of plants)

Sweden
52% (12)

Finland
33% (4)

United
Kingdom
21% (37)

Belgium
59% (7)

The Netherlands 5% (2)
Germany 28% (20)
Czechoslovakia 29% (8)
Hungary 48% (4)
Bulgaria
34% (6)

France
73% (56)

Spain
36% (9)

Switzerland
40% (5)

Former
Yugoslavia:
6% (1)

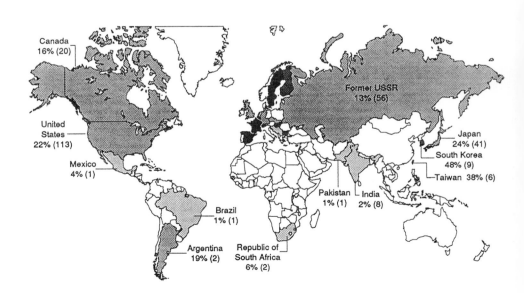

Canada
16% (20)

United
States
22% (113)

Mexico
4% (1)

Brazil
1% (1)

Argentina
19% (2)

Republic of
South Africa
6% (2)

Former USSR
13% (56)

Japan
24% (41)

South Korea
48% (9)

Taiwan 38% (6)

Pakistan
1% (1)

India
2% (8)

Status of Nuclear Power Development

Today nuclear power plants, operating in 32 countries, supply more than 17% of the world's electricity. In 1992 there were at least 411 reactors operating, with a net electrical power capacity of over 320,000 megawatts.[1] Another 71 plants, 60,000 megawatts, are being constructed, and 59 plants that would add another approximately 47,000 megawatts are in various stages of planning.[2] Fifty-seven reactors that provided power in the past are now permanently shut down. The plants currently operating have reactors supplied by 40 different vendors, although because of mergers and international agreements, the effective number is significantly smaller.

Essentially all the reactors can be classified into six different types: PWRs, BWRs, GCRs, PHWRs, LWGRs, and LMRs. In terms of deployment, the PWR dominates. The balance is divided among BWRs, PHWRs, GCRs, and LWGRs. LMRs (breeders) have had no real effect on the power supply yet. GCRs exist predominantly in the United Kingdom; LWGRs are indigenous to the former USSR. Neither of these two reactor types is included in future development plans. The United States has the most reactors operating; France generates the highest percentage of electricity by nuclear power.

Electrical generating plants do not operate at 100% of their rated electrical output all of the time. Plants must be shut down periodically for refueling and scheduled maintenance, and while in opera-

The United States has the most reactors operating; France generates the highest percentage of electricity by nuclear power.

---

[1]"World List of Nuclear Power Plants," *Nucl. News* (August 1992).

[2]*World Nuclear Industry Handbook 1992. Nucl. Eng. Int.* (1992).

Total MW(e) of Nuclear Electric Capacity*

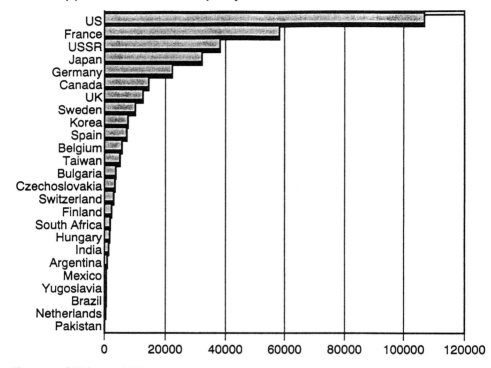

*Status as of 31 August 1991

Source: World Nuclear Industry Handbook 1992. Nucl. Eng. Int. (1992).

Reactor Classifications

Reactor Type	Fuel	Moderator	Coolant
PWR: pressurized water reactor	Enriched uranium	Light water	Light water
BWR: boiling water reactor	Enriched uranium	Light water	Light water
GCR: gas-cooled reactor	Natural or enriched uranium	Graphite	Carbon dioxide
PHWR: pressurized heavy water reactor	Natural or slightly enriched uranium	Heavy water	Heavy water
LWGR: light water graphite reactor	Enriched uranium	Graphite	Light water
LMR: liquid-metal reactor	Enriched uranium or plutonium	None	Sodium

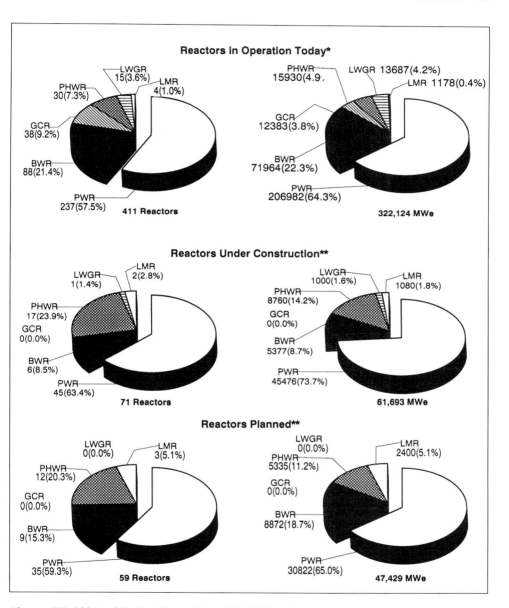

Source: "World List of Nuclear Power Plants," *Nucl. News* (August 1992).

**Source: World Nuclear Industry Handbook 1992. Nucl. Eng. Int. (1992).

Status of Early Demonstration Reactors

Country	Reactor	Type	Year in Service	Status
Canada	Rolphton NPD	PHWR	1962	Shut down 1987
	Douglas Point	PHWR	1968	Shut down 1984
	Gentilly 1	PHWR	1972	Shut down 1977
	Pickering 1	PHWR	1971	Operable
	Pickering 2	PHWR	1971	Operable
	Pickering 3	PHWR	1972	Operable
	Pickering 4	PHWR	1973	Operable
France	Marcoule G2	GCR	1959	Shut down 1980
	Marcoule G3	GCR	1960	Shut down 1984
	Chinon A1	GCR	1964	Shut down 1973
	Chinon A2	GCR	1965	Shut down 1985
	Phénix	LMR	1974	Operable
United Kingdom	Calder Hall 1	GCR	1956	Operable
	Calder Hall 2	GCR	1957	Operable
	Bradwell 1	GCR	1962	Operable
	Bradwell 2	GCR	1962	Operable
	Berkeley 1	GCR	1962	Shut down 1989
	Berkeley 2	GCR	1962	Shut down 1988
	Dounreay PFR	LMR	1975	Operable
United States	Shippingport	PWR	1957	Shut down 1982
	Dresden 1	BWR	1960	Shut down 1978
	Yankee Rowe	PWR	1961	Shut down 1991
	Hallam	LMGR	1963	Shut down 1964
	Elk River	BWR	1963	Shut down 1967
	Piqua	OMR	1963	Shut down 1965
	LaCrosse	BWR	1969	Shut down 1987
	BONUS	BWR	1964	Shut down 1968
	Big Rock Point	BWR	1963	Operable
	San Onofre 1	PWR	1968	Operable
	Connecticut Yankee	PWR	1968	Operable
	Fermi 1	LMR	1966	Shut down 1972
	Nine Mile Point	BWR	1969	Operable
	Peach Bottom 1	HTGR	1967	Shut down 1974
	CTVR	PHWR	1964	Shut down 1967
	Pathfinder	BWR	1966	Shut down 1967
USSR (former)	Beloyarskiy 1	LWGR	1964	Shut down 1983
	Beloyarskiy 2	LWGR	1969	Shut down 1989
	BN-600	LMR	1981	Operable
	BN-350	LMR	1973	Operable

Source: "World List of Nuclear Power Plants," *Nucl. News* (August 1992) and *World Nuclear Industry Handbook 1992. Nucl. Eng. Int.* (1992).

St. Lucie nuclear generating station with its two 839-MW(e) PWRs at Hutchinson Island, Florida. Unit 2 had the highest capacity factor, 100.2%, for any reactor in 1991. (Courtesy of Florida Power and Light Company)

France's Gravelines nuclear generating station with its six 910-MW(e) PWRs. (Courtesy of Electricité de France)

The Perry power plant, in North Perry, Ohio, contains two units. Unit 1, a 1205-MW(e) BWR, went into operation in 1987; Unit 2 construction has been deferred. (Courtesy of The Cleveland Electric Illuminating Company)

The Heysham II power station consisting of two of the last AGRs ordered. Both of the two 615-MW(e) reactors entered service in 1988. (Courtesy of Nuclear Electric)

Percent of Electricity Generated by Nuclear Power in 1990

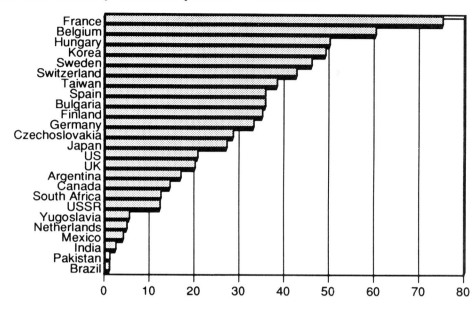

Source: World Nuclear Industry Handbook 1992. Nucl. Eng. Int. (1992).

The Largest Reactors

Reactor Type	Net MW(e)	Plant	Country
PWR	1335	Saint Alvain 1 & 2	France
	1455	(under construction) Chooz B1, B2, and Civaux	France
BWR	1260	Kruemmel	Germany
	1315	(under construction) Kashiwazaki Kariwa 6 & 7	Japan
PHWR	881	Darlington 1 & 2	Canada
LWGR	1380	Ignalia 1 & 2	Lithuania
GCR (AGR)	700	Torness 1 & 2	United Kingdom
LMR	1200	Creys-Malville (Super Phénix)	France

Source: "World List of Nuclear Power Plants," *Nucl. News* (August 1992).

Number of Reactors in Operation*

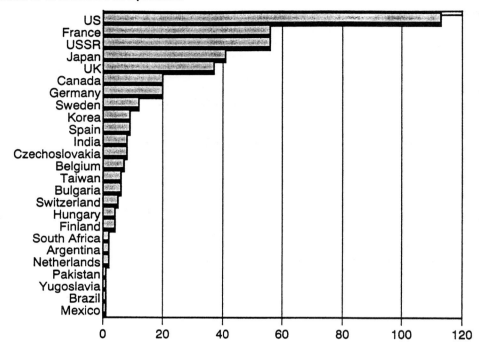

*Status as of 31 August 1991

Source: World Nuclear Industry Handbook 1992. Nucl. Eng. Int. (1992).

tion, some must follow the variation in demand for electrical energy with time of day. The capacity factor, defined as the ratio of the average power level of a plant over a time period to the rated power level of the plant, is generally used to describe performance. During 1991, approximately 46% of the nuclear plants recorded capacity factors exceeding 75%. An additional 37% of the plants exceeded 50% capacity factors.[3] Lifetime capacity factors are available for the water-moderated reactors and two types of British gas-cooled reactors. PWRs and PHWRs lead with approximately 67%. The BWR is only slightly behind at 64%. The old Magnox gas-cooled reactors have averaged 59%, while the newer advanced gas-cooled reactors have only managed 42%. The leading

---

[3]Laurie Howles, "1991 Annual Review of Load Factor Trends," *Nucl. Eng. Int.* (April 1992).

National Lifetime Capacity Factor

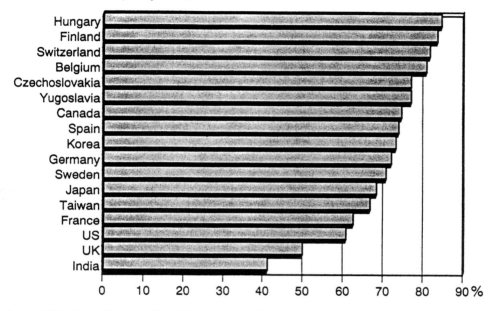

Source: "1991 Annual Survey of Load Factor Trends," *Nucl. Eng. Int.* (April 1992).

reactor for 1991 was the St. Lucie 2 PWR of the Florida Power & Light Company, which achieved a capacity factor of 100.2% by operating slightly above its rated power. Hungary, Finland, Switzerland, and Belgium have achieved national lifetime capacity factors exceeding 80% for operation of their LWRs.

BIBLIOGRAPHY

Howles, Laurie. April 1991. "1991 Annual Review of Load Factor Trends," *Nucl. Eng. Int.*

Leclercq, Jacques. 1986. *The Nuclear Age.* Sodel.

———. August 1992. "World List of Nuclear Power Plants," *Nucl. News.*

———. 1992. *World Nuclear Industry Handbook 1992. Nucl. Eng. Int.*

Cobalt-60 being used to produce gamma radiographs of welds. (Courtesy of AEA
Technology)

FIVE

Other Peaceful Applications of Nuclear Energy

No one could have foreseen the multitude of beneficial applications that were made possible by the success of the CP-1 experiment. James Chadwick discovered the neutron in 1932, ten years before CP-1, and we have known about naturally occurring radioisotopes for more than a century. But soon after CP-1, special-purpose research reactors made copious supplies of neutrons and radioisotopes available for the first time. It is the availability of these elementary particles and radioactive atoms that opened up new fields of scientific research and the development of nuclear technologies.

For most people, the first nonpower nuclear application that comes to mind is nuclear medicine. Today about one-half of all hospital patients are diagnosed or treated using some form of nuclear medicine. But radioisotopes are also important in manufacturing, consumer products, emergency lighting, remote power sources, insect control, food preservation, sterilization of medical supplies, and many areas of research. Neutrons are an excellent complement to x rays for peering inside solid objects, whether for a better basic understanding of high-temperature superconductivity or searching for defects in airplane wings.

Radioisotope Applications

Radioisotopes were made available in large quantity for the first time by the exposure of elements to neutrons in nuclear reactors and as by-products of the fission process. Even the earliest reactors could create neutron fluxes several orders of magnitude higher than had been possible with radium-beryllium sources. Of the roughly 1600 isotopes that have been studied by nuclear science, approximately 1300 are radioactive. We have entered the age of tailored isotopes in which an isotope for a particular application can be chosen based on chemical behavior, type and energy of radiation, and half-life.

Radioisotopes in use today are produced from a variety of sources. Such naturally occurring isotopes as Be-7, C-14, and U-235 each have at least one beneficial application. The roles of U-235 in nuclear reactor fuel and C-14 in radiocarbon dating are well known. Beryllium-7 transported from the atmosphere by rain is used by environmental scientists in studying deposits in stream beds. Even radioisotopes dispersed in the atmosphere from bomb tests and the Chernobyl nuclear accident have been used to study unrelated global environmental issues. But most radioisotopes in use today have been produced by fission in research reactors or by irradiation of selected targets in reactors or accelerators. A small sampling of the application of these isotopes is given below.

Medicine

Nuclear medicine is the field of medical science that uses radiation from radioisotopes to diagnose or treat diseases. Today virtually all major hospitals have nuclear medicine departments. More than 10 million nuclear imaging procedures are performed each year in the United States alone. The principal reason for the exceptional growth of nuclear medicine is that it provides a means for physicians to assess whether an organ or body system is functioning properly without using an invasive procedure. A healthy organ can be distinguished from a diseased one, and the nature and specific location of the disease can often be determined much earlier than with other methods. Two technical developments have enabled the benefits of nuclear medicine to become generally available to patients: (1) hospital, university, and commercial reactors and accelerators that make radioisotopes readily available for the production of radiopharmaceuticals and (2) advanced imaging and computer systems to unfold and interpret data from the radiation emitted by the radiopharmaceutical.

Even before radioisotopes became plentiful enough for routine use in medical treatment, they had become important research tools in the study of biology and medicine. Today their use in research is more important than ever. The development of most new drugs relies on radioactive tracers to study the metabolic pathways of the drug in the body.

The first application of radioactive tracers to biological research was in 1923 by Georg Karl Hevesy, a Hungarian chemist who later became known as the "father of nuclear medicine." Hevesy investigated the distribution of lead in bean stems and roots by using minute amounts of Pb-210 and Pb-212. In 1937, Glenn Seaborg discovered I-131 that had been produced in a cyclotron, and later was a codiscoverer of Co-60 and Tc-99m. Cobalt-60 has been used for decades as a source for external-beam radiation therapy; today it is often used to sterilize medical supplies. Iodine-131 has essentially replaced surgery for treatment of thyroid cancer. Technetium-99m is now the most commonly used

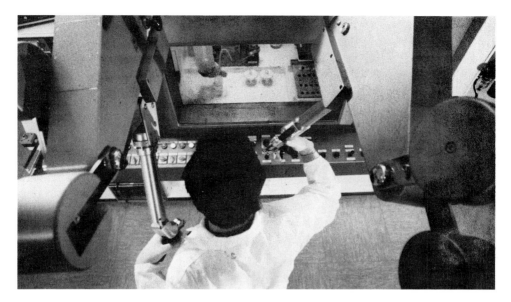

Preparation of Tc-99m for use as a radiopharmaceutical. (Courtesy of U.S. Council for Energy Awareness)

diagnostic radionuclide. Hevesy received the Nobel Prize for chemistry in 1943 for his work; Seaborg captured the prize in 1951 for his discoveries in the chemistry of transuranic elements. Ten of the past 15 Nobel prizes in medicine and physiology have been awarded for research that involved the use of compounds labeled with radioisotopes.

The key to using radionuclides in medicine is to select an isotope that emits the right type of radiation at the right energy, decays away quickly after its useful work is done, and can be concentrated in the human organ of interest. This is done either by choosing an element that naturally concentrates in the correct body system, such as iodine in the thyroid gland, or, in a process called *labeling,* by attaching the radionuclide to a compound that does concentrate in the proper organ. In diagnostic procedures, the physician relies on the emission of discrete-energy gamma rays (photons) that can be detected outside the body. In medical treatment procedures, the radioisotopes emit charged particles that can deliver a large radiation dose to the cancerous cells without needlessly irradiating surrounding tissue. Effective treatment of a malignant tumor can require a radiation dose 10 to 100 times larger than would be lethal if it were received throughout the patient's body.

Gamma cameras, consisting of very large sodium-iodide crystals, collimators, and banks of photomultiplier tubes, measure emissions of unattenuated photons within a narrow energy range. The data are analyzed to create a two-

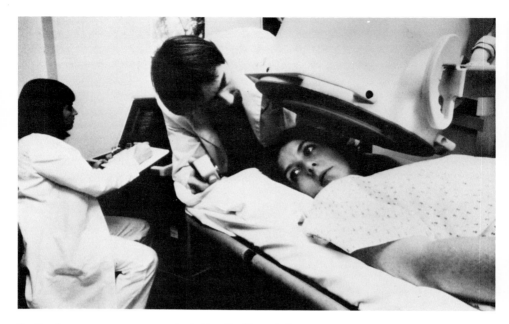

Positioning a gamma camera for taking Tc-99*m* scintigraphs of a patient. (Courtesy of U.S. Council for Energy Awareness)

dimensional image of the emission sites in a process known as *scintigraphy*. If one image after another is formed of the same region of the body, a dynamic history of the radiopharmaceutical biokinetics can be recorded. This is the process used millions of times each year in cardiac stress tests.

By taking data from different angles of rotation around a patient, three-dimensional views inside the body can be obtained in a process called *tomography*. In single-photon emission computed tomography (SPECT), the gamma camera is rotated around the patient. In positron emission tomography (PET), a stationary array of cameras is used for coincidence detection of the two 511-keV photons produced by positron/electron annihilation. Light radioisotopes such as C-11, N-13, O-15, and F-18 are produced in cyclotrons for use as positron (antielectron) emitters in PET scans. Both PET and SPECT are used in physiological studies of healthy individuals, particularly for research into how the brain functions. In patients, these tomography techniques can be used to identify and study tumors, strokes, dementia, epilepsy, depression, drug abuse, and amnesia.

Beta emitters are chosen for radiopharmaceuticals used in disease treatment because the beta energy is absorbed within a very small volume around the emission site. By far the most successful application of radionuclide therapy has been for the treatment of hyperthyroidism and thyroid cancer with I-131. A promising new form of treatment involves labeling monoclonal antibodies that attach only to specific forms of cancer with such radionuclides as Y-90, I-131, and Re-186. Cancers of the colon, ovaries, and liver, as well as lymphomas and melanomas, are being treated with labeled monoclonal antibodies as a part of ongoing research. Some treatments do not effect a cure, but are used to reduce a patient's pain and dependence on narcotics to control the pain. Samarium-153, Re-186, and Re-188 are used to reduce extreme pain in bone cancer patients.

Industry

The application of radio-isotopes in manufacturing often relies on the attenuation of radiation as it passes through a product. Radioisotopes can be used in this way to monitor and control thicknesses in the manufacture of plastics, paper, and photographic film, as well as the amount of glue on a postage stamp and the amount of sugar in consumer foods. Radiography is used to inspect metals and machines for flaws and

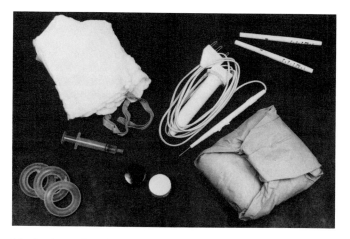

Medical supplies that have been sterilized with radiation. (Courtesy of SteriGenics)

cracks in structural materials, welds, and cast metals. Some applications of radiography, such as inspection of the Alaskan pipeline, have received considerable attention. However, few consumers are aware that the engine block, pistons, air bags, tires, and aluminum wheels of their new automobiles are more reliable because of radiography. While radiography can be done with x-ray machines in many instances, Co-60 sources are used when the photons must be more penetrating, when portability is important, or if cost is a major factor. In other applications, radioisotopes are used to help set up manufacturing processes or as a quick and reliable way to test trial products.

The Am-241 in home smoke detectors generates enough ionization in the air within a small chamber to allow a battery to drive a small electric current using the air as a conductor in one leg of the circuit. Smoke entering the chamber impedes the current, which in turn triggers an alarm.

Other common consumer products take advantage of radioluminescence, in which the energy released by the radioactive decay of tritium, an isotope of hydrogen, is converted to light. Examples of consumer products using tritium include luminous watch dials and rifle sights, as well as exit signs aboard aircraft and ships and in many buildings. More extended use of radioluminescence is made for emergency lighting on offshore oil rigs and in lifeboats, and for runway lights on remote Alaskan airfields.

Powerful radioactive heat sources using Pu-238 or Sr-90 have been used to produce electricity for remote applications in space, at weather stations at the North and South poles, at remote seismic sensing stations, and on the ocean floor.

Agriculture

Radioisotopes have been dramatically successful in controlling many types of insect pests that destroy crops or livestock. In the procedure for insect control, thousands of male insects raised in a laboratory are sterilized by exposure to gamma rays from a radioisotope such as Co-60. The infertile males are released in infested fields to mate with healthy females, resulting in many eggs that do not hatch. Since the life cycle of many insect pests is short, populations are quickly reduced or even eliminated. Screw worms were eliminated in the southeastern United States in the 1950s; Mediterranean fruit flies were controlled in California in the 1970s; and mosquitos, tsetse flies, horn flies, and melon flies have been controlled in several countries around the world. When this technique can be used in place of chemical pesticides, it offers a major environmental advantage because no harmful residues are left on the crops.

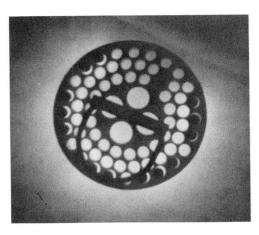

Cobalt-60 sources for gamma sterilization of commercial products. (Courtesy of SteriGenics)

Radioisotopes are also used in plant research. Radiotracers are added to chemical fertilizers to study the uptake of chemicals by plants and to determine the efficiency of fertilization. Plant seeds have been exposed to radioisotopes to speed-up the development of plants with such desirable properties as improved resistance to disease, better adaptability, and earlier ripening.

One potentially large application of radioisotopes is in the irradiation of food products to preserve them for long periods of time without significant deterioration of nutritional value. Cobalt-60 sources are used to irradiate food with penetrating gamma rays at doses large enough to destroy bacteria, viruses, molds, and insects that can cause spoilage. There are approximately 160 such facilities around the world, though not primarily for food irradiation. Sprouting of potatoes and onions can be delayed, and ripening of certain fruits can be delayed. Food can also be completely sterilized when the highest doses are used. The sterilization process is also used for facial cosmetics, contact lens solutions, and some types of medical supplies. The food irradiation technique, which makes chemical additives and refrigeration unnecessary, also requires less energy than other food preservation methods. As with all other preservation techniques and cooking, the principal nutritional drawback is the destruction of specific vitamins.

In spite of the preference of astronauts for food preserved by irradiation, the process has made little real impact in the United States. In part, this is due to the overabundance of food supplies, ready availability of alternative preservation methods, and lack of public acceptance. The Food and Drug Administration has moved cautiously to approve the preservation of specific foods with irradiation. Wheat and flour were approved in 1963, white potatoes in 1964, pork in 1985, herbs, spices, seeds, teas, vegetable seasonings, fruits, and vegetables in 1986, and poultry in 1990. However, in countries where food spoilage contributes to malnutrition and lack of an adequate food supply, food preserved by irradiation has already had a great impact. Among the organizations that endorse food irradiation are the World Health Organization, the U.N. Food and Agricultural Organization, and the American Medical Association.

Space

Nuclear power is used in space[1] because other power source options simply won't work in a number of applications. Solar power cannot be used for deep-space exploration; some space probes operating nearer the sun have electrical power requirements that exclude cyclical solar exposures or the use of rechargeable batteries. For high power requirements, solar panels simply become too unwieldy. Nuclear power is the only option for a reliable, long-term, low-mass, compact power supply in space.

Two types of nuclear power sources have been used—radioisotope thermoelectric generators (RTGs) and small nuclear reactors. The United States has launched 25 nuclear power sources. Twenty-four of the power sources used one or more RTGs and there was a single nuclear reactor, the SNAP-10A. The USSR space program preferred to use Romaska or Topaz reactors starting in the late 1960s. Approximately 30 reactor-powered satellites were launched by

---

[1]This section is drawn extensively from John W. Lawrence, "Nuclear Power Sources in Space: A Historical Review," *Nucl. News* (November 1991).

the Soviet Union between 1968 and 1991. The U.S. applications have been for navigational, meteorological, and exploration programs, including six manned space missions. The most visible successes are the RTGs used in the *Pioneer* and *Voyager* satellites which are still operating, though the spacecrafts have passed the outermost reaches of the solar system. The Soviet reactors generally have powered Cosmos or Rorsat satellites, used primarily in ocean surveillance and navigation. The reactors use a thermionic principle to generate electricity directly within the core.

An RTG contains a significant amount of Pu-238, which generates 567 watts of heat per kilogram of plutonium due to its natural radioactive decay. The heat is used to keep the systems and components on board the satellite at an optimum temperature, or to generate electricity by means of the thermoelectric effect. Depending on the number of RTGs used for a mission, from 1 to 22 kg of Pu-238 have been aboard the spacecrafts or satellites. The design of the RTGs has been improved over time to ensure safety under all conditions, including possible launch accidents and reentry impact. Current designs maximize immobilization of the plutonium during all mission phases, including consideration of postimpact environmental degradation of the containment.

> **The design of the RTGs has been improved over time to ensure safety under all conditions, including possible launch accidents and reentry impact.**

SNAP-10A, the experimental nuclear reactor that powered the Snapshot satellite launched by the United States in 1965, used approximately 30 kg of U-235 as a fuel and sodium-potassium as a working fluid circulating between the reactor and a thermoelectric power conversion device, which contained no moving parts. Strict precautions were taken to ensure safety during prelaunch activities of the SNAP-10A reactor. Only when the satellite achieved a circular orbit of 1300 km above the earth were the signals sent from earth to initiate the procedures necessary to take the reactor critical and eventually to power. The reactor operated successfully for 43 days, until it automatically shut down following an electrical problem on the satellite. It was not able to be restarted by commands from the ground.

Nuclear reactors have also been considered for space propulsion for missions in which chemical rockets were not practical. Nuclear rocket development in the United States began in 1955 with the Rover Program—a cooperative effort between the U.S. Atomic Energy Commission (AEC) and the U.S. Air Force. The Air Force relinquished its role to the National Aeronautics and Space Administration (NASA) when the new agency was formed. The program continued until 1973, when it was canceled because the human explora-

Artist's conception of the SNAP-10A reactor in orbit. (Courtesy of Rockwell International Corporation)

tion of Mars mission had been abandoned and the Saturn-V launch vehicle program was dropped.

Nevertheless, nuclear rocket technology development in the Rover Program was successful. Early research on reactor designs and fuel element materials was carried out in the late 1950s at the Los Alamos Scientific Laboratory (LASL). The nuclear rocket engines were designed to heat hydrogen to very high temperatures, allowing it to expand rapidly and be exhausted out of the nozzle of the rocket. By October 1960, the KIWI A series of reactor tests had demonstrated the feasibility of a solid core rocket by operating up to a power of 100 MW for 5 minutes. In 1961 LASL initiated the more aggressive series of KIWI B tests, which disclosed a core vibration problem that was highlighted by a spectacular failure in the KIWI B-4A test in late 1962. The problem was identified and corrected; the 1964 KIWI B-4E test was run for 10.5 minutes at a power of 1000 MW.

Based on the early KIWI successes, the Nuclear Engine for Rocket Vehicle Application (NERVA) Program was initiated in 1961. The joint AEC/NASA

Preparation for a nuclear rocket test. (Courtesy of Westinghouse Electric Corporation)

Space Nuclear Propulsion Office selected Aerojet General Corporation and Westinghouse as the contractors for the program. Overall the NERVA test (NRX) series demonstrated reactor structural integrity and reliability, stable control over a wide range of operating conditions, capability of fuel to operate above 3600°F for one hour with minimal corrosion, and analytical predictability of reactor performance. An integrated engine system test (NRX/EST) in 1966 demonstrated multiple restart capability as well as 30 minutes of operation at the full power of 1100 MW.

The use of nuclear power in space became a source of international public concern following a few well-publicized incidents. Space nuclear power has been a subject of discussion in the United Nations, to the point where legal and technical guidelines have been drafted for consideration. The United States has adopted safety criteria for RTGs that assure their survival in accidents without plutonium dispersal. Key features for the safety of space reactors are to prevent their startup until they are in a safe orbit and to assure that they are in at least a 300-year orbit at the end of service.

> **Key features for the safety of space reactors are to prevent their startup until they are in a safe orbit and to assure that they are in at least a 300-year orbit at the end of service.**

The United States and the Soviet Union both experienced failures involving space nuclear power sources. Of the four U.S. incidents, only the first incident had any safety or environmental significance. In that 1964 event, a satellite reentering the earth's atmosphere ejected its RTG over the western Indian Ocean, resulting in 17,000 curies of plutonium being dispersed in the upper atmosphere. The most publicized of the Soviet Union's incidents involved the Cosmos-854 satellite, which came out of orbit with a Romaska-type reactor aboard, containing approximately 49 kg of U-235. The partially burned satellite crashed onto the frozen Great Slave Lake in northern Canada. The cleanup operation recovered all accessible, significantly sized radioactive debris, so that there has been no long-term environmental effect. Experience from the handful of failures as well as the many successes has led to design changes and operational strategies intended to ensure the safety of future nuclear-powered space missions.

Neutron Applications

Unlike radioisotopes, the benefits of neutrons have little opportunity to be brought before the public eye. But to scientists, neutrons represent a unique research tool with which to study the basic nature of materials as well as a nondestructive assay tool with which to examine a wide variety of things. Much research relies on the neutron's ability to penetrate deep into a material and scatter out again, carrying with it information about the material.

Research with neutrons began soon after their discovery in 1932. Fermi's neutron physics work in the mid-1930s helped prepare him for the CP-1 experiment. Today the primary uses of neutrons in research are in scattering experiments, production of radioisotopes, radiography, activation analysis, and testing advanced fission and fusion reactor fuels and materials. Soon after the CP-1 experiment, reactors were being designed for special research applications. After 1970 some scattering experiments were shifted to large accelerators that produced neutrons by spallation reactions in heavy targets. More recently, accelerator facilities have turned to a hybrid technology, using fission in uranium spallation targets to boost neutron production.

Scattering Experiments

Preparation for neutron scattering measurements began soon after the CP-1 experiment.[2] At Oak Ridge, the Clinton Pile, a graphite-moderated reactor, began operation in late 1943 and CP-3, a heavy-water-moderated reactor built in the Argonne Forest near Chicago, began operation shortly thereafter. These reactors initially were used to measure nuclear cross-section data needed for the Manhattan Project. Fermi developed a device to produce monoenergetic neutrons and Walter Zinn built the first crystal spectrometer for neutrons. A paper by Fermi and Leona Woods Marshall in *Physical Review* in 1947 was the first introduction most physicists and chemists had to the potential for using neutrons to study solids. By 1951, E. O. Wollan and C. G. Shull working at Oak Ridge had established neutron diffraction as a fundamental technique for such studies.

Three properties of neutron scattering that make it an essential atomic scale probe of condensed matter are the relative weakness of the neutron/matter interactions, the neutron's magnetic moment, and the compatibility of neutron energies and wavelengths with atomic motions in solids and liquids. "Cold" neutrons, with wavelengths on an atomic scale, are produced by slowing down the source neutrons with such moderators as liquid methane or liquid hydrogen. Neutron scattering provides information about the positions of the atoms in a material as well as the motion of the atoms in response to thermal excitations. This technique is also a unique tool for studying structural and ferroelectric phase transitions.

An increasingly important application is that of determining the positions and dynamical behavior of hydrogen in materials, including polymers, water,

---

[2]G. E. Bacon, *Fifty Years of Neutron Diffraction—The Advent of Neutron Scattering*, Adam Hilger (1987).

The High Flux
Isotope
Reactor (HFIR)
used for
neutron
scattering
experiments
and the
production of
isotopes.
(Courtesy of
U.S.
Department of
Energy)

and biological layers. The application of neutron magnetic scattering can reveal the location, relative alignment, and thermal motions of spins in a magnetic material. Neutron scattering has provided the understanding of magnetic order in superconductors, random fields in antiferromagnets, spin glasses, phase transitions, one- and two-dimensional order, charge density waves, and quantum fluids.[3]

An important recent application of neutron diffraction is in the study of high-temperature superconductors. Neutron diffraction determination of several phases, their exact stoichiometry, and the locations of the crucially important oxygen atoms in the crystal lattice has contributed information essential to understanding these potentially important new materials.

[3]Paola Bisanti and S. W. Lovesey, "Condensed Matter and Materials Research Using Neutron Diffraction and Spectroscopy. Reactor and Pulsed Neutron Sources," RAL-87-029, Rutherford Appleton Laboratory Publication (May 1987).

Positioning of the Glass, Liquid, and Amorphous Materials Diffractometer (GLAD) at the Intense Pulsed Neutron Source Facility. (Courtesy of Argonne National Laboratory)

Activation Experiments

Activation experiments rely on the formation of a radioisotope when a neutron is captured by a stable nucleus. When the radioisotope decays, it has a unique gamma signature that can be readily identified by a gamma spectrometer. The process is highly sensitive and can be applied to almost every element on earth. In activation analysis experiments, the sample is briefly exposed to neutrons until it becomes slightly radioactive, then is rapidly transported to a counting chamber. The energy of the observed photopeaks and their decay rate allows all elements present to be identified, even in minute quantities.

In a second type of activation procedure, called *neutron radiography*, a beam of neutrons projected from the reactor irradiates a sample. Neutrons transmitted through the sample are captured by a foil such as indium, gadolinium, or dysprosium. Photons from the decay of the foil expose a photographic film or excite a scintillator, in either case forming an image of the sample. When scintillator screens are used, a television picture can be taken to do motion studies of fluid flowing inside an engine, or operating valves.

Activation analysis is used for many different purposes. For example, with the recent resurrection of interest in the assassination of President John F. Kennedy, it should be noted that forensic analysis of the evidence in the original investigation relied in part on neutron activation analysis. The seven bullet fragments found were conclusively shown by activation analysis to have come from only two bullets.[4] Criminal investigations frequently rely on activation analysis to provide conclusive evidence on such materials as paint, glass, tape, gunpowder, lead, and poisons.

The authenticity of old paintings has been tested using a procedure called *autoradiography*, which was developed in a cooperative effort between Brookhaven National Laboratory and the Metropolitan Museum of Art in New York. Activation of the painting allows an image to be made using the gamma emissions as a "light" source. Because gamma rays are emitted throughout the entire thickness of the painted surface, the underlying layers can be examined without damaging the painting. Often it is possible to determine if a signature has been changed, or whether the painting is a joint effort of a master and his students. The ongoing Berlin Rembrandt Research Project, a joint effort of the Hahn-Meitner-Institut and the Berlin State Gallerie, has already shown several paintings attributed to Rembrandt to have been produced by his students.[5]

---

[4] D. Allan Bromley, "Neutrons in Science and Technology," *The Nuclear Chain Reaction—40 Years Later: Proceedings of a University of Chicago Commemorative Symposium*, The University of Chicago (1984).
[5] C. O. Fischer, "Review on Autoradiography of Paintings," *Proceedings of Fourth World Conference on Neutron Radiography*, San Francisco, May 10–15, 1992.

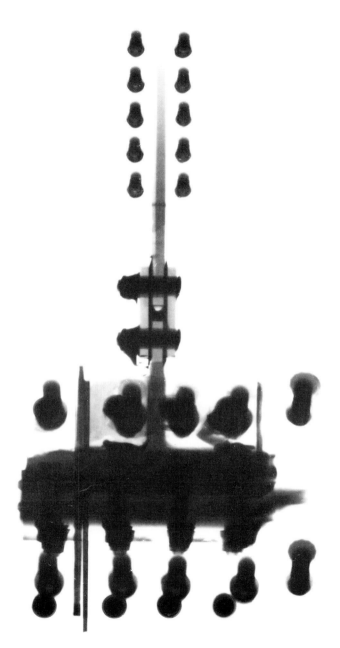

Neutron radiograph of a section from a NASA space shuttle booster. (Courtesy of Argonne National Laboratory)

Neutron radiography got its start soon after the discovery of the neutron. Kallman and Kuhn produced the first radiographs in Germany as early as 1935. However, it wasn't until 1960, when intense neutron sources were available from research reactors, that useful applications of neutron radiography were made.[6]

Neutron radiography is an excellent complement to x-ray examination of objects. While x rays are strongly attenuated by dense materials such as steel or lead, neutrons are more sensitive to lighter materials. To illustrate this point, one of the early radiographs showed the clear image of a small waxed string located behind a two-inch-thick lead block. Neutrons can be transmitted through large dense objects such as engines, aircraft wings, nuclear fuel, or metal containers for examina-

---

[6]Harold Berger, *Neutron Radiography—Methods, Capabilities, and Applications,* Elsevier Publishing Company (1985).

tion of the internal parts without the need for disassembly or any damage. As with medical imaging, successive radiographs can be taken as a subject is rotated, making three-dimensional neutron tomography possible.

Although neutron radiography is a unique, powerful examination procedure, only a handful of routine applications are in use. One of the present applications of neutron radiography is the inspection of explosives as a quality assurance step in the manufacturing process. Neutron radiography is used to look for voids or clumps in the explosive product. Prototype neutron radiograph devices are being developed and tested to search passengers' luggage for explosive devices at airports. Another major application is in the aerospace industry. Neutron radiography is used to examine the propellant in solid rocket boosters and to look for structural defects. This technique is being used to examine the turbine blades in new jet engines at an AECL facility at Chalk River, Canada. At McClellan Air Force Base in California, neutron radiography is used to detect internal corrosion in the wings and fuselages of older planes without having to disassemble them.

BIBLIOGRAPHY

Bacon, G. E. 1987. *Fifty Years of Neutron Diffraction—The Advent of Neutron Scattering.* Adam Hilgar.

Berger, Harold. 1965. *Neutron Radiography—Methods, Capabilities, and Applications.* Elsevier Publishing Company.

Bisanti, Paola, and S. W. Lovesey. May 1987. "Condensed Matter and Materials Research Using Neutron Diffraction and Spectroscopy. Reactor and Pulsed Neutron Sources," RAL-87-029. Rutherford Appleton Laboratory.

Bromley, D. Allan. 1984. "Neutrons in Science and Technology," in *The Nuclear Chain Reaction—Forty Years Later: Proceedings of a University of Chicago Commemorative Symposium.* The University of Chicago.

Cohen, Bernard L. June 1992. "Irradiated Food: Is There A Need?" *Nucl. News.*

Fischer, C. O. 1992. "Review of Autoradiography of Paintings," in *Proceedings of Fourth World Conference on Neutron Radiography,* San Francisco, CA, May 10–15, 1992.

Lawrence, John W. November 1991. "Nuclear Power Sources in Space: A Historical Review," *Nucl. News.*

——— . "Radioisotopes: Today's Applications," DOE/NE-0089, U.S. Department of Energy.

Rice, C. M., and W.H. Arnold. 1968. "Recent NERVA Technology Development," in *Proceedings of the AIAA Fourth Propulsion Joint Specialists Conference.*

Stubbs, James B., and Latresia A. Wilson. May 1991. "Nuclear Medicine: A State-Of-The-Art Review," *Nucl. News.*

Zirconium rods used in the production of cladding for LWR fuel. (Courtesy of U.S. Council for Energy Awareness)

SIX

Nuclear Fuel Technology

The 400-plus reactors producing electric power for an energy-hungry world are the most visible elements of the nuclear enterprise. But nuclear power also requires the successful development of associated fuel cycle technologies. The enrichment and reprocessing technologies developed during the Manhattan Project were technical achievements on par with the CP-1 experiment. Operation of some of the large fuel cycle facilities supporting the nuclear power plants is as complex and challenging as operation of the reactors.

Briefly, the fuel cycle consists of mining, refining, concentrating, and purifying the uranium ore, converting it to uranium hexafluoride, enriching the uranium to the desired concentration of U-235, producing the fuel elements and fuel assemblies, using the fuel in the reactor, reprocessing the fuel to recover uranium and plutonium (or alternatively storing the spent fuel), storing the waste products, and transporting materials between each of the steps in the fuel cycle. Major fuel cycle facilities have been built and operated in more than a dozen industrialized nations. However, far fewer fuel cycle facilities than power reactors have been built because international deployment of enrichment and reprocessing facilities is discouraged as a result of their potential misuse for production of nuclear weapons materials.

Fuel cycle facilities, both existing and under construction, vary substantially around the world depending on technical needs as well as national policy. Technical needs are driven primarily by the reactor types that must be serviced. National policies reflect availability of indigenous resources, nonproliferation goals, and internal political circumstances. Fuel cycle technology has its own fascinating history, but because this story is about the controlled nuclear chain reaction, the following summary of the out-of-reactor fuel cycle technologies is brief.

Mining

At an average of two to four grams per tonne, uranium is not abundant in the earth's crust. But because of its geochemical mobility, uranium has been found in ore with adequate concentration for mining in many areas of the world.

Typical ores being mined today average less than 1% uranium, although exceptional deposits of 12% in Canada and 75% in Africa have been discovered. The economic lower limit is about 0.05% unless the ore contains other valuable minerals that can be recovered.

Uranium was first recognized as an element by the German chemist Heinrich Klaproth in 1780, who was analyzing pitchblende ore from a mine that had been active for centuries. Klaproth had actually isolated uranium oxide, which he named Urania after the recently discovered planet Uranus. Uranium metal is hard, very dense, melts at 1133°C, undergoes a major phase change at 660°C, and has a very complex chemistry. The metal reacts with air to form UO_2, but uranium compounds have several degrees of oxidation. The pure metal is unsuitable for nuclear fuel; an alloy must be manufactured to obtain the desired properties. Uranium dioxide, a stable ceramic with a high melting temperature (2800°C) but poor thermal conductivity, is more often used for reactor fuel. Both common isotopes of uranium are radioactive—U-235 with a half-life of 713 million years and U-238 with a half-life of 4.5 billion years. Uranium-238 is the parent isotope of the radioactive decay chain that includes radium, radon, and polonium.

The operation of a remote-controlled front-end loader in a uranium mine. (Courtesy of U.S. Council for Energy Awareness)

The mined ore is crushed, sorted by radioactivity, then fine-crushed. Acid or carbonate leaching is used to dissolve the uranium, which is recovered by organic solvents or ion-exchange resins. The resulting uranium ore concentrate is commonly referred to as yellowcake. The yellowcake, in turn, is purified and converted to uranium hexafluoride, the feed material for enrichment plants.

Worldwide Enrichment Facilities

Country	Plant	Capacity*	Process	Status
Argentina	Pilcaniyeu-1	20	Diffusion	Operable
	Pilcaniyeu-2	100	Diffusion	Construction
Brazil	Resende	10	Jet nozzle	Construction
China	Lanchow	200	Diffusion	Operable
France	Tricastin	10,800	Diffusion	Operable
Germany	Gronau	400	Centrifuge	Operable
	KfK Nozzle Enrichment	50	Jet nozzle	Operable
Japan	Hyuga	2	Chemical	Operable
	Ningyo-Toge (pilot)	200	Centrifuge	Operable
	Ningyo-Toge (demo)	50	Centrifuge	Operable
	Rokkasho-Mura 1	150	Centrifuge	Construction
	Rokkasho-Mura 2	1350	Centrifuge	Planned
Netherlands	Almelo	1200	Centrifuge	Operable
Pakistan	Kahuta	5	Centrifuge	Operable
South Africa	Valindaba	300	Helicon	Operable
United Kingdom	Capenhurst Urenco	850	Centrifuge	Operable
	Capenhurst BNFL	650	Diffusion	Shut down
United States	Paducah	11,300	Diffusion	Operable
	Portsmouth	7900	Diffusion	Operable
	Oak Ridge	7700	Diffusion	Shut down
USSR (former)	Siberia	10,000	Diffusion	Operable

Source: World Nuclear Industry Handbook 1992. Nucl. Eng. Int. (1992).

*kSWU/yr (thousand separative work units per year).

Enrichment

Enormous effort and capital investments have been made worldwide since the 1940s to enrich the isotopic composition of natural uranium above its natural 0.71% U-235. The initial needs were for military applications requiring enrichments above 90% U-235. Since the 1950s the largest demand for enriched uranium has been for civilian central-station power reactor fuel; the most common reactors require fuel containing on the order of 3% U-235.

In 1944, electromagnetic isotope separation, using calutrons at Oak Ridge, became the first process to produce kilogram quantities of highly enriched U-235 for the Manhattan Project. Most of the world's supply of enriched uranium, however, has been produced by the gaseous diffusion process. The technology relies on the differing rates of diffusion—depending on their isotopic composition—of molecules of uranium hexafluoride gas through multiple cascades of porous barriers. The typical enrichment factor for a single

A few of the many stages in a gaseous diffusion enrichment plant. (Courtesy of Oak Ridge National Laboratory)

stage is only 1.002, requiring diffusion plants to be physically large, with high energy requirements. The first diffusion plant was put into operation at Oak Ridge in 1945. Additional plants were subsequently built in the United States and in other countries including the United Kingdom, France, the former USSR, and China.

More recently, the more advanced gas centrifuge process has been developed and deployed in the United Kingdom, Germany, the Netherlands, and Japan. Several other advanced technologies for separating uranium isotopes are being actively developed throughout the world, including aerodynamic (nozzle), laser, chemical, and plasma centrifuge processes.

Fabrication

Reactor fuel assemblies are typically left in the reactor for a few years. The reactor core is an extremely harsh environment of high temperature, high stress, and intense radiation. Reactor fuel must remain intact throughout its

lifetime, retain radio-
active products, and
provide a robust line
of defense against op-
erational upsets that
potentially could lead
to accidents. Typical
reactor fuel elements
contain uranium in ce-
ramic form, cladding
to protect the fuel ma-
terial and contain the
fission products, a gas
space to collect the fis-
sion gases, and a ther-
mal bond between the

The gaseous diffusion plant in Paducah, Kentucky. (Courtesy of
U.S. Department of Energy)

fuel and the cladding. Elements are bundled into fuel assemblies that contain
space for coolant flow. Thousands of elements typically comprise a reactor
core. The length of time the fuel assemblies can be left in the reactor core
(lifetime) is limited by depletion of the uranium and/or radiation damage to

Experiments performed at Lawrence Livermore National Laboratory using copper vapor
lasers for the development of Atomic Vapor Laser Isotope Separation (AVLIS), an advanced
enrichment technology. (Courtesy of U.S. Department of Energy)

Worldwide Fuel Fabrication Facilities

Country	Reactor Fuel	Operable*	Under Construction*	Planned
Argentina	PHWR	300		
Belgium	MOX	35		
	PWR	400		
Brazil	PWR	100		
Canada	PHWR	3250		
France	GCR	500		
	FBR MOX	25		
	PWR+PWR MOX	500		
	PWR	750		
	LWR MOX		120	
Germany	MOX	25		
	LWR	1420		
India	PHWR	385		3000
	BWR	25		
Italy	BWR	200		
	Magnox	200		
	HWR+LWR	60		
Japan	BWR	650		
	HWR+LWR	465		
	PWR	420		
	MOX	14	35	
Korea	PWR	200		
Mexico	PHWR+PWR	2		
Spain	LWR	200		
Sweden	LWR	400		
United Kingdom	AGR	330		
	Magnox	1300		
	PWR	200		
	LWR MOX			50
United States	PWR	1950		
	PWR+BWR	700		
	BWR	1100		
USSR (former)	PWR	700		

Source: World Nuclear Industry Handbook 1992. Nucl. Eng. Int. (1992).

*Capacity in tonnes of heavy metal of fuel produced annually.

the cladding. Lifetime energy output of a fuel assembly is usually expressed as thermal energy (megawatt-days) released per unit mass (tonnes of heavy metal—uranium—in the fuel), written MWd/t.

Production of LWR fuel assemblies. (Courtesy of U.S. Council for Energy Awareness)

Fabrication of fuel elements for light water reactors is accomplished by forming fuel pellets from blended powders of uranium oxide, which are pressed and sintered into small cylinders about one centimeter in diameter and somewhat longer. Uranium oxide is stable in water, so that small breaches in the cladding are relatively benign. Tubes made from Zircaloy—zirconium alloyed with small amounts of tin, nickel, chromium, and iron—are used as cladding for the fuel. Zircaloy absorbs few of the neutrons in the reactor core and has the advantage of being less permeable than stainless steel to tritium, the radioactive form of hydrogen. Helium is used to provide the thermal bond and equalize the pressure. In Europe and Japan a few reactors are being

A tray of annular MOX fuel pellets for use as part of a core demonstration experiment in the Fast Flux Test Facility liquid-metal reactor. Each small pellet represents the energy equivalent of approximately 12 barrels of oil. (Courtesy of Westinghouse Hanford Company)

licensed to operate with mixed uranium-plutonium oxide (MOX) fuel. The present lifetime limit for light water reactor (LWR) fuel is of the order of 33,000 MWd/t.

Fabrication of mixed-oxide fuel elements for liquid-metal reactors (LMRs) is comparable to that used for LWR MOX fuel elements, except that the enrichment is much higher—20% or more depending on the size of the reactor. LMRs use stainless steel cladding. LMRs are operated at much higher power densities because the liquid-metal coolant is more effective at carrying the heat away. Today, LMR fuels routinely achieve burnups of 100,000 MWd/t, with experimental assemblies being taken to the 200,000 MWd/t range.

Gas-cooled reactors require fuel types that are substantially different from LWR fuel. Because neutrons require many collisions in graphite to reach thermal equilibrium, the ratio of graphite to uranium in GCRs must be very large, resulting in reactors with massive cores that operate at low power density. The only GCRs successfully deployed on a sizable scale were the graphite-moderated, CO_2-cooled reactors built in the United Kingdom and France. Because the original fuel was not enriched, it was necessary to have the uranium concentrated in thousands of rods broadly spaced within the graphite matrix. In such an arrangement, fast fission neutrons can escape from the fuel and be moderated in the graphite, thus avoiding "resonance" absorption by the U-238 during the slowing down process. Once thermalized, the neutrons have a sufficiently high probability of fissioning U-235 to maintain the chain reaction. A low-absorption magnesium alloy, Magnox, for cladding the uranium was the breakthrough needed to allow the commercial generation of electricity with these reactors, which were originally designed to produce plutonium. Later, uranium oxide enriched from 1 to 2%, clad in stainless steel, was used in "advanced" GCR fuels. GCR fuel rods have been designed with a variety of complicated surface geometries to improve the thermal efficiency of the systems. On-line refueling helped these reactors achieve reasonable capacity factors.

A small number of high-temperature gas-cooled reactors have been demonstrated. In these designs, the CO_2 coolant, chemically stable only below 540°C, is replaced with helium, which is not reactive even at the 800+°C operating temperature of some designs. To improve heat transfer, the surface area of the fuel is expanded many times by dispersing the uranium in the form of tiny refractory-coated particles sintered into carbon-graphite rods that fit snugly within massive graphite blocks. The helium coolant flows through separate holes drilled in the blocks. The fuel particles are the fuel "elements" of the reactor, in that they contain the fission products within refractory coatings of pyrolytic graphite and silicon carbide that serve as a "cladding." On the order of one billion of the fuel particles, which are only a few hundred microns in diameter, may be needed to fuel a single reactor. HTGR concepts call for uranium enriched to at least 20%. Lifetimes of over 100,000 MWd/t are expected with this fuel.

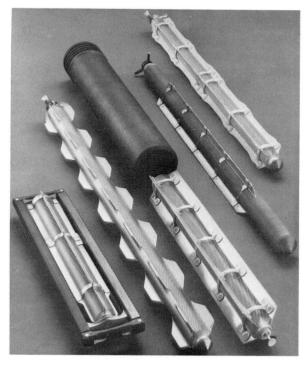

Evolution of British gas-cooled reactor fuel elements. The design requirements included reducing the heat transfer film temperature drop, improving coolant mixing, locating the fuel in the channel, and reducing fluid dynamic induced flutter. From the left, the elements are Berkeley, Sizewell, Hunterston with sleeve, PIPPA-Mark II, and Oldbury. (Courtesy of British Nuclear Fuels plc)

Reprocessing

Fuel reprocessing began in the United States in the late 1940s when the bismuth phosphate process was installed in a Hanford production plant for separation of kilogram amounts of plutonium from uranium. This process was supplanted by more efficient countercurrent extraction processes, which included the Redox

Refractory coatings on an encapsulated HTGR fuel kernel. (Courtesy of General Atomics.)

Worldwide Commercial Reprocessing Facilities

Country	Plant	Capacity (tonnes-HM/year)	Fuel Type Processed	Status
Argentina	Ezeiza	5	Oxide	Construction
Belgium	Mol	100	Oxide	Shut down
France	La Hague UP2	800	Oxide, MOX	Construction
	La Hague UP3	800	Oxide	Operable
India	Kalpakkam 1	125	Oxide	Operable
	Tarapur	100	Oxide	Operable
	Trombay	50	Oxide	Operable
	Kalpakkam 2	1000	Oxide	Construction
Italy	Saluggia	10	Oxide	Operable
Japan	Rokkasho-Mura	800	Oxide	Construction
United Kingdom	Dounreay	8	FBR MOX	Operable
	Sellafield (Magnox)	1500	U metal	Operable
	Sellafield (THORP)	1200	Oxide	Construction

Sources: World Nuclear Industry Handbook 1991 and 1992. Nucl. Eng. Int. (1991 and 1992); Simon Rippon, "First Phase of New Reprocessing Plant Opened at La Hague," *Nucl. News* (June 1992).

process in the United States, the Butex process in England, and the Trigly process in Canada. All of these were superseded by the Purex process in the early 1950s. Purex has since been employed in nearly all the major reprocessing plants in the world, both for recovery of plutonium from production reactors and spent fuel discharged from civilian power reactors.

Nonaqueous processes were also developed during the 1960s. A process in which separations were based on the different volatilities of fluoride compounds of the fuel constituents was dropped for lack of industrial interest. Development of pyrochemical processing, or pyroprocessing, which uses molten-metal and molten-chloride salt systems, was dropped for a number of years. Development of pyroprocessing resumed in the United States in 1984 for application to metal-fueled sodium-cooled reactors.

Aqueous fuel reprocessing involves three stages: dissolution of the fuel in nitric acid, separation of the uranium and plutonium from fission products and other contaminants, and recovery of the solid fuel product.

The earliest aqueous reprocessing technology was the bismuth phosphate process, developed for the Manhattan Project at the University of Chicago's Metallurgical Laboratory and demonstrated on a pilot-plant scale at Oak Ridge. It was put into full-scale operation at Hanford in 1945, only four years after the first laboratory experiments. Working with only microgram quantities, the necessary discoveries in the chemistry of plutonium were made under the leadership of Glenn Seaborg. Seaborg later went on to become chairman of the Atomic Energy Commission.

Glenn Seaborg in 1946. (Courtesy of Argonne National Laboratory)

The bismuth phosphate process recovered plutonium at an overall efficiency of greater than 95% and decontaminated it from fission products by a factor of 10^7. However, the serious disadvantages of the process, including batch operation, inability to recover uranium, the large amount of process chemicals required, and a large volume of process wastes, soon spurred development of new, more efficient processes. Attention was focused on solvent extraction processes of the type that were already in use for recovery of uranium from ore leach liquors. These processes offered the advantages of continuous operation, large decontamination factors, and uranium recovery.

The first solvent extraction process, Redox, was developed at Argonne National Laboratory. Redox was installed by the General Electric Company at the Hanford plutonium plant in 1951 and used for several years. The disadvantages of the Redox process were the volatility and flammability of the solvent and the large amount of aluminum nitrate in the aqueous waste stream.

Meanwhile the search for organic extractants turned up many that were effective for separating uranium, plutonium, and fission products and suitable for process application. The Canadians developed the Trigly process in which triglycol dichloride was used in a head-end cycle; subsequent purification cycles used hexone as in the Redox process. The British developed the Butex process, which employed dibutyl carbitol as a solvent and which had an

Piping in a Purex reprocessing plant. (Courtesy of Cogema)

advantage over the Redox process in that nitric acid alone was a satisfactory salting agent.

The Purex process emerged in 1949 as a result of initial development work at Knolls Atomic Power Laboratory. The solvent for this process is tributyl phosphate, which has a strong chemical affinity for uranium and plutonium and is able to extract their nitrate salts from nitric acid solutions. The advantages of the Purex process over earlier processes are elimination of the aluminum nitrate salting agent, lower solvent volatility and flammability, high chemical and radiation stability of the solvent, and lower operating costs. After pilot-plant scale demonstration at Oak Ridge National Laboratory, the Purex process was installed in plutonium-production plants at the Hanford facility and at Savannah River in South Carolina. Subsequently, the process was installed in plutonium separation plants throughout the world, including France, the United Kingdom, the former Soviet Union, Germany, and India.

The first commercial fuel reprocessing plant was the NFS (Nuclear Fuel Services, Inc.) facility built in West Valley, New York. The plant, which was designed to have a processing capability of one tonne of nuclear fuel per day, operated between 1966 and 1972. A one tonne/day plant was built by GE at Morris, Illinois, but was never operated because of startup difficulties. Today it is used to store discharged light water reactor fuel assemblies. Construction of a larger (five tonne/day) central processing plant by Allied General Nuclear

Services was begun at Barnwell, South Carolina. Although construction of the Barnwell plant was essentially completed in the late 1970s, it was never operated because of presidential directives. Presidents Ford and Carter suspended commercial fuel reprocessing as an example of their concern with the large amount of high-purity plutonium that would be made available through fuel reprocessing and might be diverted to construction of nuclear weapons. Although President Reagan removed the ban on commercial reprocessing, there are no plans to do so. The Barnwell plant is used only to store spent fuel assemblies.

Purex reprocessing of discharged reactor fuels has been pursued vigorously by several countries, notably France, the United Kingdom, Japan, and India. France constructed a large reprocessing complex at La Hague, which processes fuel discharged from the reactors of

Unloading of a dry cask at La Hague reprocessing plant in France. (Courtesy of Cogema)

several countries. Today, France is the world leader in providing commercial reprocessing services. When upgrades to the UP2 facility are complete and UP2 800 joins UP3 at La Hague, French LWR reprocessing capacity will be at 1600 tonnes of heavy metal per year, enough to serve the needs of 60 to 80 LWRs. The United Kingdom, which has continued to recover spent fuel discharged from its own nuclear power reactors, has recently built the large THORP (Thermal Oxide Reprocessing Plant) facility at Sellafield, which will also sell services to other countries. Japan's large reprocessing plant is scheduled to begin commercial operation in 1995. India has considerable experience

United Kingdom's Sellafield facility, the site of the Thermal Oxide Reprocessing Plant (THORP). Magnox fuel has also been reprocessed at Sellafield for more than 30 years. (Courtesy of British Nuclear Fuels plc)

with the Tarapur Fuel Processing Plant, and is building a large facility at Kalpakkam.

Transportation

Spent nuclear fuel and wastes from reprocessing plants are transported in massive, well-engineered shipping casks. These casks are designed to withstand even the most severe road accidents. International regulations require a regimen of drop, fire, submersion, and crash tests before any cask is certified for use. In addition to providing accident protection, the casks are designed to protect workers from the radiation sources inside. Consequently, shipping casks are heavy, some weighing more than 100 tonnes.

The integrity of a spent fuel cask is demonstrated during a test in which a high-speed train crashes into it. (Courtesy of U.S. Department of Energy)

Spent fuel is normally stored in a water pool at the reactor site for at least a year before shipping. After one year, the residual power from fission products in a spent PWR fuel assembly is approximately 6 kW. Casks are designed to transmit the heat from the fuel to the outside air by natural processes such as thermal conduction and natural convection.

Waste Management

The issue of disposing of nuclear wastes has grown to dominate all other nuclear fuel cycle issues in most of the nations with active nuclear power programs. Yet if today's heated controversy over disposal of nuclear waste had been postulated to Enrico Fermi and the other early pioneers, they almost certainly would have been surprised. The early view (and one still prevalent in the scientific and engineering community) was that two of the most positive attributes of nuclear power were clean electrical energy and a highly concentrated waste form.

The nuclear fuel cycle produces several classes of radioactive waste. Each has its own characteristics that determine the regulations that govern its treatment, storage, transport, and final disposal. Spent fuel assemblies can be considered waste just as they come out of the reactor, or they can be repro-

Nevada's Yucca Mountain, the prospective site for the U.S. geologic repository for high-level waste. (Courtesy of U.S. Council for Energy Awareness)

cessed to recover the valuable nuclear fuel material and reduce the waste volume. Although at current uranium prices, reprocessing and fabrication of MOX fuel elements are not economically justified, most countries capable of doing so have elected to proceed with reprocessing on the basis that it will be required eventually, and that it improves nuclear waste management. The United States is the notable exception.

High-level waste, as the name implies, is characterized by a high level of radioactivity. Cooling is required to remove heat generated by radioactive decay. Most high-level waste originates from fission products extracted during reprocessing of spent fuel. All countries generating high-level waste have selected deep geologic disposal as the preferred method of isolating the waste. The waste is immobilized in glass monoliths, which are then placed in corrosion-resistant canisters. The canisters are then placed in deep, stable geologic formations.

The siting of high-level waste disposal repositories requires intensive characterization of candidate sites and final selection of the most suitable site.

Most countries are finding great difficulty in obtaining public support or even acceptance of siting decisions. In the United States, for example, the Department of Energy (DOE) has selected Yucca Mountain in Nevada as a potential repository site, but determined opposition by local groups and officials has repeatedly delayed DOE's schedule for detailed characterization of the site. The table "Worldwide Status of Disposal of High-Level Nuclear Wastes" makes it clear that the inability to progress on a geologic repository is symptomatic of most nuclear power programs.

Current U.S. policy is that spent commercial fuel is regarded as high-level waste and is to be ultimately disposed in a deep geologic repository yet to be constructed. Many scientists and engineers view this as throwing away a valuable energy resource. The DOE is required by law to provide monitored retrievable storage (MRS) capability to enable interim off-site storage of spent fuel, pending availability of geologic disposal. An Office of Nuclear Waste Negotiator has been established to find technically suitable areas of the country willing to host an MRS.

Transuranic waste is characterized by concentrations of long-lived alpha-emitting nuclides with atomic numbers greater than uranium. The long half-lives, typically millions of years, of the radionuclides comprising transuranic waste require isolation in geologic repositories comparable to those specified for disposal of high-level waste. The United States has constructed the Waste Isolation Pilot Plant (WIPP) in a deep salt formation in New Mexico to store transuranic wastes from government programs, but opening of that facility is also being delayed.

Low-level wastes require little shielding or remote handling for worker protection. The largest volumes of low-level wastes, and the largest amounts of radioactivity in the wastes, originate from the nuclear power industry. The other principal sources of low-level wastes are medical institutions and research laboratories. Low-level wastes are commonly disposed of in near-surface landfills. Liquids are solidified before disposal. The wastes are commonly immobilized in concrete or resin, placed in a suitable container, and buried under several feet of earth. Low-level disposal facilities are available at numerous sites in the United States and elsewhere around the world.

Worldwide Status of Disposal of High-Level Nuclear Wastes

Country	Responsible Agency	Fuel (tonnes HM/yr)	Disposal Plan	Progress to Date
Belgium	National Agency for Radioactive Waste (ONDRAP/NIRAS)	140	Reprocessing. Vitrification. Deep disposal.	No sites selected. Research and survey at laboratory at Mol. Preliminary Safety Assessment report ~ 1997.
Canada	Waste producers	1300	Repository 500–1000 m in granite.	Panel reviewing environmental assessment submitted by AECL. Studies at Cigar Lake uranium deposit and underground laboratory at Lac du Bonnet.
Finland	Waste producers, through Nuclear Waste Commission (YJT)	69	Direct deep disposal.	Five sites under preliminary investigation. Feasibility studies submitted 1982, 1985. Development work approved 1987.
France	National Agency for Radioactive Waste Management (ANDRA)	1100	Reprocessing. Repository 400–1000 m deep.	Sites selection for investigation halted in 1991.
Germany	Federal Ministry for Environment (BMU)	495	Reprocessing followed by deep disposal. Direct deep disposal being considered.	Gorleben site investigation for waste. Pilot spent fuel conditioning plant being constructed there.
Japan	Japan Nuclear Fuels Company (JNFS)	740	High-level vitrified waste from reprocessing stored 30–50 years, then deep disposal.	Two plans to build underground research laboratories have been halted by local opposition.
Korea	Korea Atomic Energy Research Institute (KAERI)	242	Reprocessing and direct disposal under consideration. Reprocessing forbidden by current agreement.	Site selection for interim storage stopped by local opposition in 1990.
Netherlands	Central Organization for Radioactive Waste (COVRA)	15	Interim storage followed by direct disposal.	Preliminary geological studies carried out in cooperation with other countries.
Spain	National Waste Management Company (ENRESA)	187	Interim storage followed by direct disposal. Vandellos 1 fuel must be reprocessed.	Site-independent design completed.
Sweden	Swedish Nuclear Fuel Waste Management Company (SKB)	230	Direct disposal in copper canisters 500 m below ground.	Feasibility studies completed. Hard rock laboratory is under construction at Aspo Island. Two to three sites to be investigated.
Switzerland	Producers, through the National Cooperative for the Storage of Radioactive Waste	85	Reprocessing. Vitrification. Deep disposal. Interim storage and direct disposal considered.	Areas of suitable rock formations being investigated. Interim storage at Beznau. Wurenlinge storage site being licensed.
United Kingdom	British Nuclear Fuels (BNFL)	1000	Reprocessing. Vitrification. Interim storage for AGR fuel starting 1993.	Full-scale vitrification began at Sellafield in 1991. THORP construction complete.
United States	Department of Energy (DOE)	2200	Interim storage followed by direct geological disposal.	Preliminary investigation for MRS sites to begin soon. Site characterization studies for Yucca Mountain geological repository under way.

Source: "Spent Fuel Management and Transport," *Nucl. Eng. Int.* special supplement (May 1992).

Summary of Treatment and Disposal Methods for Low-Level and Intermediate-Level Wastes

Country	Estimated Waste (m³)	Treatment or Disposal Method
Argentina	22,000	Storage, incineration
Belgium	63,250	Storage, incineration, repository
Brazil	22,000	
Bulgaria	41,250	Storage
Canada	198,000	Storage, incineration, repository, burial
CIS (former USSR)	715,000	Storage, burial
China	3,300	Burial
Cuba	4,950	
Czechoslovakia	66,000	Storage, repository
Finland	27,500	Storage, repository
France	687,500	Storage, incineration, burial
Germany	327,550	Storage, incineration, burial
Hungary	19,250	Storage, repository
India	27,500	Storage, incineration, repository, burial
Italy	35,750	Storage, incineration, burial
Japan	367,500	Storage, incineration, burial
Korea	88,000	Burial
Mexico	16,500	
Netherlands	5,500	Storage, repository
Pakistan	1,650	
Poland	11,000	Storage
Romania	24,750	Storage, incineration
South Africa	22,000	Repository, burial
Spain	82,500	Storage, incineration, repository
Sweden	110,000	Storage, incineration, repository
Switzerland	33,000	Incineration, repository
Taiwan	55,000	
United Kingdom	98,250	Storage, incineration, repository
United States	1,200,000	Storage, incineration, burial
Yugoslavia	5,500	Storage, repository

Source: special supplement to *Nucl. Eng. Int.* (February 1991).

BIBLIOGRAPHY

Leclercq, Jacques. 1986. *The Nuclear Age.* Sodel.

———. *The Modular High Temperature Gas-Cooled Reactor: Inherently Safe Nuclear Power.* General Atomics.

———. February 1991. Special supplement to *Nucl. Eng. Int.*

Rhodes, Richard. 1986. *The Making of the Atomic Bomb.* Simon & Schuster.

Rippon, Simon. June 1992. "First Phase of New Reprocessing Plant Opened at La Hague." *Nucl. News.*

———. May 1992. "Spent Fuel Management and Transport." *Nucl. Eng. Int.*

———. 1991 and 1992. *World Nuclear Industry Handbook. Nucl. Eng. Int.*

Oklo, Gabon, the site of nature's prehistoric nuclear chain reactor. (Courtesy of Electricité de France)

SEVEN

Nuclear Safety

Scientific, industrial, and political leaders involved with the peaceful development of nuclear energy understood from the very beginning that safety was essential to the success of the new technology. While sound radiation protection standards were not fully developed at the outset, the importance of isolating workers, the public, and the environment from radioactive materials was recognized. Further, it was clear that the peaceful benefits of nuclear power should be shared among nations, and that technical assistance with the development of civilian nuclear power programs might be used as an incentive to accept international safeguards, thus discouraging the spread of nuclear weapons. It was also known that nuclear energy would have to be economically competitive for any large-scale deployment to occur. However, the early developers of nuclear energy were aware that they could not predict all the problems the budding technology eventually would face.

One of those problems has turned out to be public concern over nuclear energy—a technology that scientists see as safe, nonpolluting, and capable of enriching the lives of people in many areas of the world.

President Eisenhower's "Atoms for Peace" speech on December 8, 1953, opened the door to domestic and international development of nuclear energy. By that time, a large amount of data was already available from programs on nuclear safety sponsored by the handful of nations with active development programs. The United Nations sponsored its first conference on the "Peaceful Uses of Atomic Energy" in Geneva in 1955. No less than 200 (out of a total of 1132) papers on nuclear safety and protection of the environment, and a comparable number of papers on medical uses of radiation, were presented at the conference.

> As they were leaving Stagg Field after the CP-1 experiment, Crawford Greenewalt said to Enrico Fermi, "We've talked about many problems that we may run into; which do you think we should worry about the most?"
>
> Fermi responded, "We should worry about the ones that we haven't talked about."[1]
>
> ———
>
> [1]University of Chicago.

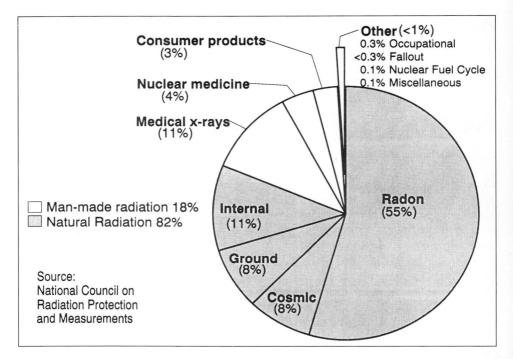

Relative importance of different sources to the average radiation exposure of the U.S. population. (Courtesy of U.S. Department of Energy)

Radiation

Any concern over nuclear safety is based on the potential for release of radiation or radioactive materials. The design and operation of nuclear power plants is intended to prevent harmful releases under all circumstances, from normal operation to highly improbable accidents. Nevertheless, radiation is an inevitable by-product of nuclear power as well as a natural component of our environment. The fraction of our annual radiation exposure that comes from the generation of electricity by nuclear power is approximately 0.1%, which is insignificant relative to even the variations in the background of natural radiation.

Radiation and its effects on man continue to be the subjects of study by researchers and review by prestigious scientific panels. The annual average exposure from natural radiation for a typical American was estimated to be about 100 millirem per year until 1987, when it was revised upward to 360 millirem because of a new appreciation for the contribution from naturally occurring radon gas. Of the 360 millirem, 18% comes from man-made radiation, primarily from voluntary exposure associated with medical procedures.

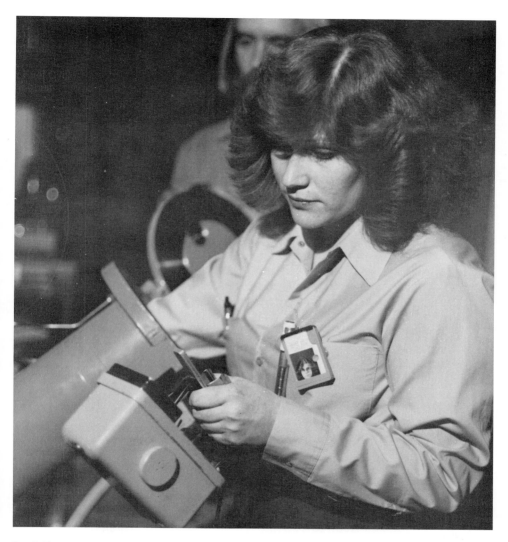

Radiation fields are carefully measured to protect workers in the nuclear industry. (Courtesy of Argonne National Laboratory)

Consumer products such as smoke detectors and luminous watch dials contribute about 3% of the exposure. Fallout from atmospheric testing of nuclear weapons accounts for less than 0.3%. The natural radioactivity in our own bodies contributes approximately the same amount that we receive from medical x rays. Cosmic radiation, streaming in from outer space, averages 8% of the total.

Individual radiation doses are unevenly distributed, depending on where we live, types of houses and work buildings, types of medical treatment, frequency of high-altitude flights, and other factors. The 0.1% of the average exposure due to the nuclear fuel cycle is received almost entirely by workers in the industry; the rest of the population gets effectively nothing from the generation of nuclear power.

Most data on the adverse health effects of radiation have come from studies of the survivors of the atomic bombs dropped on Hiroshima and Nagasaki. Individuals receiving short-term exposure to radiation on the order of 100 rem (100,000 millirem) are subject to acute illness. Acute exposures of 500 rem are sufficient to kill a substantial fraction of individuals within weeks. But there is controversy in how to extrapolate back by a factor of 1000 or more to the very low dose rates associated with normal living, medical treatment, and occupational exposure. One theory is that the effect is linear, allowing a simple extrapolation to be done. A second theory is that there is a threshold below which there is effectively no damage, or the damage is such that it can be repaired by the body. A small minority holds the view that low radiation doses actually cause proportionately more damage. Regardless of which theory is correct, the radiation emitted from operation of a nuclear plant is far too insignificant to have any impact on public safety.

It might be expected that because there is such a large variation in state-to-state natural radiation exposure, the importance of low radiation doses could be inferred from state-to-state variations in the cancer rate. But the states with the highest radiation exposures happen to have the lowest cancer rates. The risk of cancer from normal radiation exposure is simply insignificant compared to such other causes as smoking, industrial pollution, and life-style.[2]

Reactor Safety

In the United States, the government sponsored aggressive reactor safety experiments prior to the start of commercialization activities. Approximately 900 square miles of isolated desert land in Idaho were selected to be the site for the National Reactor Testing Station. One reason for selection of this remote location was so that any accidental release of radioactive materials from tests to study reactor accidents would not affect the public. Safety testing continued well after the commercial nuclear power era began, often with international partners. Other Western nations recognized the imperative of safe operation of nuclear power plants and conducted independent reactor safety experiments. The safety philosophy that evolved in the former Soviet Union and Eastern European nations was apparently less conservative, but there is a

[2]Adnan Shihab-Eldin, Alexander Shlyakhter, and Richard Wilson, "Is There a Large Risk of Radiation? A Critical Review of Pessimistic Claims," ANL-92/23, Argonne National Laboratory (1992).

Early safety experiments in BORAX demonstrated the self-regulating features of the BWR concept. (Courtesy of Argonne National Laboratory)

current initiative to "upgrade" some Soviet-built reactors to Western operating and design standards. Nevertheless, some Soviet-built PWRs such as those in Finland and Hungary have excellent records for operating efficiency.

The early development period in the United States was characterized by a broad-based AEC program that included uranium exploration, enrichment, power reactors, space propulsion, waste management, biology, medicine, and peaceful applications of nuclear explosions. The parallel naval reactors program focused on production of nuclear propulsion systems. Development of safety technology was a key focus of the U.S. Atomic Energy Commission's (AEC's) civilian and naval reactor programs. Radiation-effects biology programs were carried out; fundamental and applied nuclear data were generated; a number of special safety-experiment reactors were built and operated; and several series of major reactor safety experiments were carried out. Fundamental radiation standards for all radiation applications were developed.

Defense in Depth

The defense-in-depth philosophy involves a series of several physical barriers and multiple levels of protection[3]:

- The radioactive fission products are at the center of the physical barriers and levels of protection.
- The first physical barrier is the fuel material itself. Most fission products are bound within the fuel "matrix."
- The fuel cladding forms the second physical barrier. It is intended to retain all the fission products and to isolate the fuel from the coolant.
- The third physical barrier is the primary coolant system boundary. In most reactors today, this is a high-pressure steel vessel and pipe system.
- The confinement is a fourth physical barrier, which is provided unless it has been shown that the function has been provided by another means. All U.S. reactors have containment buildings to provide this confinement.
- The first level of protection is the combination of conservative design, quality assurance, surveillance activities, and a general safety culture.
- The second level of protection is control of operation, including response to abnormal operation or to any indication of system failure. This level of protection is provided to ensure the continued integrity of the first three physical barriers.
- The third level of protection includes engineered safety features and protective systems provided to prevent the evolution of failures of equipment and personnel into accidents (or more severe accidents) and to retain radioactive materials within the confinement.
- The fourth level of protection incorporates those measures, including accident management, that are directed toward preserving the confinement.
- The fifth level of protection is off-site emergency response, aimed at mitigating the effects of the release of radioactive materials to the environment.

[3]*Basic Safety Principles for Nuclear Power Plants,* International Atomic Energy Agency (1988).

From the very beginning, reactor designers understood that a nuclear power plant could not explode like a nuclear bomb—the hazard was from the "ashes" of the chain reaction, i.e., the fission products. Reactor safety was based on containment of any credible release of radioactive material. The concept of "defense in depth" became standard practice to meet the general nuclear safety objective, which is to protect individuals, society, and the environment by establishing and maintaining in nuclear power plants an effective defense against radiological hazard.[4] First and foremost, defense in depth emphasizes the importance of preventing accidents. However, in the event of an accident, defense in depth emphasizes mitigation of damage and doing everything possible to minimize injuries to workers and the public. This philosophy has continued to evolve over the years into internationally accepted basic safety principles.

[4]*Basic Safety Principles for Nuclear Power Plants,* International Atomic Energy Agency (1988).

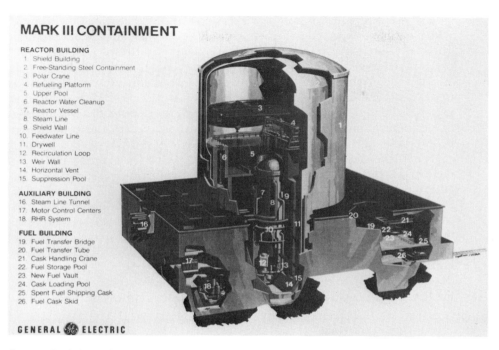

MARK III CONTAINMENT

REACTOR BUILDING
1. Shield Building
2. Free-Standing Steel Containment
3. Polar Crane
4. Refueling Platform
5. Upper Pool
6. Reactor Water Cleanup
7. Reactor Vessel
8. Steam Line
9. Shield Wall
10. Feedwater Line
11. Drywell
12. Recirculation Loop
13. Weir Wall
14. Horizontal Vent
15. Suppression Pool

AUXILIARY BUILDING
16. Steam Line Tunnel
17. Motor Control Centers
18. RHR System

FUEL BUILDING
19. Fuel Transfer Bridge
20. Fuel Transfer Tube
21. Cask Handling Crane
22. Fuel Storage Pool
23. New Fuel Vault
24. Cask Loading Pool
25. Spent Fuel Shipping Cask
26. Fuel Cask Skid

GENERAL ⊛ ELECTRIC

Conceptual view of a reactor building with its defense-in-depth safety features. (Courtesy of U.S. Department of Energy)

In 1957 the first bounding estimates of the consequences of a large nuclear accident, based on an arbitrarily large release of fission products, were published by the AEC in a landmark report called WASH-740. It was not until 1975, when WASH-1400 (better known as the *Reactor Safety Study*, or Rasmussen report, after MIT Professor Norman Rasmussen who headed the study) was issued, that a truly quantitative estimate was available for the probability of a major reactor accident in a U.S. nuclear plant. Over the years, the Reactor Safety Study has been challenged by a number of critics, and new safety issues requiring investigation have arisen, but nothing has happened to change the basic conclusions of the report.

In any type of risk analysis, consequences become more severe as more and more improbable circumstances and events are postulated. For most reactor accidents, WASH-1400 showed that the most probable result would be property damage to the plant, but no deaths or acute illnesses due to radiation exposure of workers or the public.[5]

---

[5]Ralph Lapp, *The Nuclear Controversy*, Fact Systems (1974).

The worst type of reactor accident is the so-called reactor "meltdown," which might be expected to happen once in 20,000 years of reactor operation. The study showed that there would be no detectable deaths in 98 out of 100 reactor meltdowns, over 100 detectable deaths in only 1 out of 500 meltdowns, and 3500 detectable fatalities in only 1 out of 100,000 meltdowns. In addition to deaths immediately attributable to the accident, the cloud of radioactive material released in some cases would expose a large population to small doses of radiation. Using the conservative linear extrapolation model for radiological effects, some small fraction of the population would be expected to develop cancer. The average impact would be 400 fatalities over several decades. For the worst meltdown accident considered, there would be an estimated 45,000 additional cancer deaths in an affected population of ten million people. This corresponds to an increase in the probability of an individual's dying from cancer by about 0.5%, which is significantly less than the state-to-state variation in the normal cancer mortality rate. If there were a reactor meltdown every five days, the effect would be comparable to the estimated 30,000 deaths in the U.S. each year as a result of pollution from burning coal.[6]

Antinuclear activists often talk only of the most severe postulated accident, the 1 case in 100,000 meltdown accidents, leaving the impression that all major

Containment tests include the impact of a plane crash. (Courtesy of U.S. Department of Energy)

---

[6]Bernard Cohen, *The Nuclear Energy Option*, Plenum Press (1990).

reactor accidents would result in disaster. Clearly, with fewer than 500 nuclear power plants operating worldwide, there are not going to be 100,000 reactor meltdown accidents, or even 100. The equivalent cannot be said of other energy technologies. There have been incidents such as dam failures and excessive pollution that have caused a large number of fatalities. Perhaps the best known incident happened in 1952, when pollution from coal burning under unusual atmospheric conditions in London caused 3500 fatalities within a few days.

People are subject to all types of risks, which can best be understood in relative terms. For example, a person would have a 20,000 times greater chance of being killed by lightning than by the largest reactor accident described above. If all electricity in the U.S. were generated by nuclear power, it would represent the same risk as a regular smoker indulging in an extra cigarette once every 15 years, as an overweight person putting on an extra 0.012 ounce, or increasing the highway speed limit from 55 to 55.006 miles per hour.[7] For any reactor accident, the probability of occurrence is much less than other man-made or natural accidents with similar consequences. The relative risk of nuclear power, to either workers or the public, is simply quite small.

The type of analysis that went into WASH-1400 has continued to be refined. The U.S. Nuclear Regulatory Commission (NRC) now encourages all nuclear utilities to conduct probabilistic risk assessments (PRAs) that are plant-specific. The largest benefit from these expensive and lengthy studies has been the ability to identify the systems or operations that pose the most risk for bringing about an accident. Money for modifications and maintenance can then be effectively directed, resulting in real safety improvements. As a result, today's plants, even older ones, pose less risk than the plant used in the Reactor Safety Study.

Reactor Accidents

There have been two major accidents in nuclear electrical generating stations plus a major accident at a large plutonium-production reactor.[8] There have also been a number of lesser accidents with no off-site consequences, a substantial number of accident "precursors"—events that could lead to an accident if corrective action were not taken, and a few serious accidents at government-owned nuclear facilities. Each significant event provided infor-mation that helped make nuclear power safer, and in the case of the major accidents, resulted in changes in design or operational procedures to help prevent similar events in the future.

---

[7]Bernard Cohen, *The Nuclear Energy Option*, Plenum Press (1990).
[8]Edward Edelson, *The Journalist's Guide to Nuclear Energy*, U.S. Council for Energy Awareness (1988).

Three Mile Island nuclear generating station with Unit 2, the site of the 1979 accident, on the left and Unit 1 still in operation on the right. (Courtesy of GPU Nuclear Corporation)

The first major accident happened at Windscale on the coast of England in 1957 when the graphite moderator in a large plutonium-production reactor caught fire and burned for about two days. The incident occurred during a routine heat-treating process to reduce the radiation-induced swelling of the graphite. When carbon atoms are displaced by neutron scattering in a graphite matrix, swelling results and there is a buildup of potential energy, known as *Wigner energy* (after the great physicist Eugene Wigner). Heating the matrix to a certain level reduces the swelling and releases the Wigner energy in a controlled manner. In the Windscale incident, the energy release was too rapid, which caused further heating of the matrix and an acceleration of the process. Eventually the graphite caught fire and burned some of the natural uranium fuel rods. After attempts to smother the fire with inert gases failed, the fire was extinguished with water.

Exhaust gases from the Windscale facility were filtered, but volatile radio-active iodine and cesium isotopes escaped to the surrounding countryside. Milk from cows on the 200 square miles surrounding the plant was banned from human consumption until the end of the month. The extent to which the health of local residents was damaged by the accident is still a matter of controversy. As a result of lessons learned from the accident, procedures for annealing the graphite and dealing with graphite fires were improved. Air cooling was replaced by pressurized CO_2 in the later reactor designs. Today the area is known as Sellafield, the site of thriving nuclear activity, including the new THORP reprocessing facility.

In 1979, a complex sequence of events at the Three Mile Island Reactor Unit 2 (TMI-2) led to a classic core damage accident. The incident began when the coolant water to the PWR was inadvertently cut off. Pressure in the reactor vessel quickly increased, causing the reactor to shut down automatically, and a safety relief valve to open. The reactor operators, overwhelmed by information from hundreds of display panels in the control room, did not understand what was happening. The automatic relief valve failed to close after the pressure was reduced, and water poured out through the opening. The emergency core cooling system (ECCS) responded automatically, as was intended, to keep the core covered with water. However, the operators, not recognizing that the relief valve was open, manually shut off the ECCS to prevent too much water from going into the core. Two hours elapsed before their mistake was discovered. Water continued to escape from the reactor, while the remaining water started to boil. The water level dropped below the top of the core, causing the fuel elements to heat sufficiently to cause serious damage, releasing fission products. Some of the radioactive material escaped through the valve into the containment building, and some fission products were transported by coolant water into storage tanks in an auxiliary building. A few curies of radioactive gases passed through the containment building's charcoal filters into the open air.

The TMI-2 event demonstrated the containment of even extreme accidents in properly designed plants. In effect, it was an exceptionally expensive, but thorough, reactor safety experiment. The wisdom of the defense-in-depth philosophy was validated; the multiple barriers and levels of protection proved their worth in protecting the health of the public and the workers. Practical lessons were learned in terms of instrumentation requirements, equipment qualification, operator training, and owner/operator accountability. The most valuable lesson learned from TMI-2 was the importance of providing the operators with accurate and complete information on the status of the plant, as well as thorough training to understand all the data. Great strides have since been made through programs such as operator training and awareness, maintenance, and operating experience case studies. These industry-sponsored efforts have been guided by the

> The wisdom of the defense-in-depth philosophy was validated; the multiple barriers and levels of protection proved their worth in protecting the health of the public and the workers.

Modern control rooms, such as the one in the Diablo Canyon nuclear generating station, provide operators with information to handle normal and unusual operating conditions. (Courtesy of Pacific Gas and Electric Company)

Institute of Nuclear Power Operations (INPO), which was set up by nuclear utilities to improve nuclear plant operations. The damaged TMI-2 core and other components have long since been removed for scientific investigation. After modifications and numerous qualification steps, the sister reactor, TMI-1, was allowed to restart and today is an efficiently running plant.

In 1986, the Chernobyl accident occurred at a four-reactor power station near Kiev in the Ukraine. The Chernobyl reactors are of the water-cooled, graphite-moderated (LWGR) type, specifically known as RBMK-1000. Their design is substantially different from anything that exists in the Western world. Two design features that greatly affected the accident were lack of a containment building and a "positive feedback coefficient." The latter simply means that the reactor is not self-regulating. If the coolant water boils or is otherwise lost, the power of the reactor increases rather than decreases. Both of these design features violate the defense-in-depth principle. RBMK reactors were originally designed as dual-purpose plants to produce power and weapons plutonium, which accounts for some of the unusual features of their design.

The damaged Chernobyl power plant before Unit 4 was buried in concrete. (Courtesy of Tass/Sovfoto)

The Chernobyl accident was set up when technicians took several important safety systems out of service in order to perform a test on the reactor at low power (approximately 20% of maximum). Several instabilities in the reactor were encountered during the course of the test, but that was not considered unusual because of the normal difficulty of controlling the RBMK-1000 at low power. Finally, at one point in the test, too little water was being pumped into the core to keep it cool; steam pressure in the core rose rapidly, causing a runaway power surge because of the positive feedback. The control rods, which had been removed from the core to enable performance of the test, could not be reinserted quickly enough to prevent the accident.

Two explosions blew the top off the reactor building. The sudden release of steam apparently caused the first explosion; ignition of hydrogen generated by reaction of the steam with the overheated fuel rods is thought to have caused the second explosion. As in the case of Windscale, the graphite in the reactor core caught fire and burned for several days, only more severely. However, unlike Windscale, with the top of the reactor building gone, the smoke from the fire carried away 50 million curies of radioactive materials directly into the atmosphere. The fire was eventually extinguished by dumping boron, dolomite, lead, sand, and clay from helicopters. The core has since been entombed in a concrete sarcophagus.

More than 200 firefighters and other workers were hospitalized for radiation exposure and burns. Thirty-two of them died within a few weeks; the others were released after they recovered. More than 100,000 nearby residents were evacuated without the aid of a previously developed plan; many of them have not been allowed to return to the contaminated evacuation zone. The other three Chernobyl reactors resumed operation following the accident. Estimates of health effects from the cloud of radiation that drifted over the Ukraine and over parts of the rest of the world differ substantially. A U.S. Department of Energy study places an upper limit on the maximum effect of 56,000 excess global deaths in the next 70 years for an affected population of 3.5 billion people. Statistically, 600 million normal cancer deaths would be expected to occur within the same time frame for a population of this size. Based on the maximum effect for the entire affected population, the average increase in cancer risk for an individual would be approximately 0.002%. However, for the 16,000 people living from two to six miles from the plant, the increase in cancer risk is estimated to be about 4%.

News of the accident gave many Western scientists their first inkling of the design and operating conditions that led to the Chernobyl catastrophe. The accident underscored several key safety design principles and emphasized the need for a worldwide commitment to the basic principles of reactor safety in nuclear power plant design and construction. The world's reaction to the Chernobyl accident opened up lines of communication between East and West to help ensure that the mistakes that led to the Chernobyl accident were not repeated. The World Association of Nuclear Operators (WANO) has been established to implement effective exchanges. A number of initiatives are under way to determine what changes are needed to improve safety in Soviet-designed reactors and how best to implement them.

Nonproliferation

Once the cloak of secrecy was lifted by the Atoms for Peace initiative, the overriding concern was how to encourage civilian nuclear applications for power production, medicine, and food supply while at the same time preventing countries that were given access to peaceful nuclear technology from starting nuclear weapons development programs. It was recognized that heavily industrialized nations that chose to make weapons development a national priority could do so with their own internal resources if they were determined enough to stand up to the international attention such overt activity would generate. The real challenge was to prevent the surreptitious development of weapons by nations that imported nuclear technology. This dilemma led to the creation of the International Atomic Energy Agency (IAEA) in 1956 to assure that the development of nuclear power was limited to peaceful applications. Many non-nuclear weapons countries voluntarily agreed to accept safeguards inspections of their nuclear facilities in exchange for assistance with development of their civilian nuclear power programs.

In the 1960s, negotiations started on a Non-Proliferation Treaty (NPT) in which voluntary restraint from the production of nuclear weapons would be backed up by IAEA inspections. Protracted negotiations eventually opened up all areas of the nuclear fuel cycle to development by signatories, provided that no nuclear explosives would be produced. The NPT became effective on March 5, 1970, after ratification by three nuclear weapons powers—the United States, the Soviet Union, and the United Kingdom—and 40 non-nuclear weapons countries. By summer 1992, some 150 countries had signed the treaty, and those having nuclear installations were submitting to verification by the IAEA safeguards system. Among the most recent signatories are France and republics of the former Soviet Union.[9]

Nonproliferation efforts have had reasonable success, although concerns persist.[10] Only one previous non-nuclear weapons state is known to have exploded a nuclear device. India's "peaceful" explosion of a test nuclear device in 1974 spurred a renewed international effort to ensure that improved technical and institutional measures are enforced. In 1981, an Iraqi research reactor nearing completion of construction was attacked by Israeli warplanes and destroyed, marking the first time that force had been used in pursuit of nonproliferation. In 1992, Iraq, a party to the NPT, was again in the news when IAEA inspectors discovered evidence of covert production of highly enriched uranium and acquisition of nuclear weapons components.

Significant progress has been made in halting "vertical proliferation," as the mounting stockpile of weapons by nuclear superpowers was described by the non-weapons states. In 1963, the Soviet Union and the United States signed a treaty to halt atmospheric testing of nuclear weapons. Starting in 1969, the two countries entered into negotiations to limit the stocks of strategic nuclear weapons, leading to the Strategic Arms Limitation treaties (SALT) of 1972 and 1979, although the latter was never ratified by the U.S. Senate. Within the last year, Russia and the U.S. have made historic agreements to slash nuclear stockpiles within the decade to a small fraction of their present size. Anticipation of the return of sizable quantities of plutonium from weapons dismantlement has inspired a number of proposals on how best to use or store the material.

---

[9]U.S. Arms Control and Disarmament Agency.
[10]Bertrand Goldschmidt, *The Atomic Complex*, American Nuclear Society, La Grange Park, IL (1982).

Early experiments studied salt formations for suitability as nuclear waste depositories. (Courtesy of Oak Ridge National Laboratory)

Environmental Protection

In the absence of reactor accidents, the only pathway for radioactive materials to reach the environment is through nuclear waste. Most radiation decays away naturally in a relatively short time, but there are some fission products (e.g., Cs and Sr) that remain hazardous for a few hundred years, and an even smaller group of transuranic materials that stay radioactive for thousands of years. After the fission products decay, this last group poses only one to two orders of magnitude more radiological risk than the original uranium ore. The basic waste management strategy was developed early: Store the material to allow the short-lived material to decay; provide a container and waste form (e.g., borosilicate glass) that will hold the remainder for hundreds of years; and put this residue and its container in a place that is at least as isolated as where the ore originated (geologic disposal). The basic concept remains valid today.

The strategy of geologic disposal received a boost when French scientists discovered that nature had sustained a nuclear chain reaction in an especially rich natural uranium ore body in Oklo, Gabon.[11] The event happened far enough back in time, perhaps as much as 1.5 billion years, that the U-235 content of natural uranium ore was much higher than it is today. When water seeped into the ore deposit, the moderation was sufficient to sustain the chain reaction until heat boiled the water away. More water seeped in and the process repeated itself for centuries, until enough fission had occurred to drop the U-235 content below the critical level. Evidence of the "reactor" was noticed when the ore assay showed a U-235 content well below the expected 0.7%. Supporting the case for the effectiveness of geologic isolation, studies at the Oklo mine revealed clear evidence that the long-lived waste products from the Oklo reactor did not migrate significantly over their entire lifetime.

A few countries have been successful in finding and characterizing secure geologic formations for nuclear waste repositories. The United States has found and used secure formations for petroleum storage, but efforts to characterize the geologic stability of formations such as Yucca Mountain for potential storage of nuclear wastes have been frustrated by local opposition. Other nations have experienced similar delays in completing implementation of their nuclear waste plans.

In the United States, the search for a political solution to the civilian nuclear waste issue has been hampered by the record of waste accumulation from the production of nuclear weapons. The Waste Isolation Pilot Plant (WIPP), located 2150 feet below ground in the 2000-foot-thick Solado salt formation of New Mexico, has been ready to receive transuranic waste from defense programs for about one year, but opening of the facility has been thwarted by political opposition. Reports[12] from Russia during the last two years describe major environmental contamination from dumping waste from weapons production at Chelyabinsk-65, Krasnoyarsk-26, and Tomsk-7. While the legacy from the arms race has little to do with the careful control of wastes produced in civilian applications of nuclear energy, the two are difficult to separate in the eyes of the public.

During the 1960s, a nonradiological environmental concern developed about nuclear power plants. The issue—thermal pollution—applied to any type of generating station that boiled water to produce electricity, whether by burning fossil fuels or fissioning uranium. Power plants of any type are not 100% efficient; only 30% to 40% of the total thermal energy produced is converted to electricity. The balance is waste heat. The technical fix for both

[11]Jacques Leclercq, *The Nuclear Age*, Sodel (1986).
[12]Edith M. Lederer and Sergel Shargorodsky, "The Soviet Nuclear Legacy," Associated Press Report (July 1992).

nuclear and fossil fuel plants was to install cooling towers, which have become the dominant architectural signature of power plant sites. Thermal pollution was brought to national attention by local public response to waste heat discharge into a small Connecticut river, marking the first occasion where public participation affected a major design decision.

More recently, concern over the greenhouse effect has raised the issue of whether nuclear energy could reduce this environmental concern by displacing some of the fossil fuels that produce carbon dioxide. A related earlier concern had to do with easing problems with acid rain thought to be caused by burning coal with a high sulfur content. In France, and some other parts of Europe, the benefits of producing more than 50% of the national electricity by nonpolluting nuclear power are acclaimed. As communications with Eastern Europe have opened up, the extensive heavy industrial pollution caused by burning fossil fuels without effective controls has become sadly evident—in marked contrast to some Western neighbors. The environmental benefits of displacing coal for electricity production are evident even without the greenhouse concern.[13] The human risks of doing without additional electrical energy and its associated economic benefits are much higher still.

Regulation

The nuclear industry is regulated by independent federal agencies. In the United States, the NRC fills this role. The NRC was created in 1974 when the AEC was split into the Energy Research and Development Administration (ERDA, which later became the Department of Energy) and a separate regulatory agency. A very strong and prescriptive regulatory framework developed to assure that plants are designed, constructed, and operated with ample regard for safety. NRC representatives are present on each plant site. The NRC has the authority to levy substantial fines against utilities that fail to operate their plants within prescribed limits. The NRC also establishes standards and guidelines for the use of radioactive materials, and it administers a research program to help provide a foundation for some regulatory activities. Agencies similar to the NRC exist in most countries with nuclear power programs. Requirements for international nuclear commerce are set by the IAEA.

Encouraged and expected by the NRC, self-regulation within the nuclear industry has grown appreciably in recent times. Creation of the INPO organization in the United States following the TMI-2 accident was noted above, as was the founding of WANO following Chernobyl.

Supporters of nuclear power in the United States have long sought to streamline the regulatory process that was established by the AEC and evolved under the NRC. Until recently, licensing was a two-step process

---

[13]Bernard Cohen, *The Nuclear Energy Option*, Plenum Press (1990).

wherein a construction permit was needed prior to starting construction, and an operating license was needed before power could be produced. Many people feel the two-step licensing process, both with opportunities for public hearings and appeals, goes far beyond what is needed to guarantee that public concerns are addressed.

In 1989, the NRC simplified the process by issuing a new rule (10CFR Part 52) that allows utilities to obtain early site approval well in advance of intended construction, allows reactor vendors to obtain certification of plant designs, and allows plant owners to seek a combined license. Full public participation is included in both early site permits and in certification of a design. A certified design built on a permitted site could then be granted a combined license without additional hearings. The NRC has discretionary authority to determine whether and how any further hearings might be held. The U.S. Congress has legislation pending that would make this process a law.

Certified reactor plant designs have been an elusive goal of the U.S. nuclear industry. Other countries, most notably France and Canada, have enjoyed much more success in achieving a standard design. It has often been said that U.S. reactor plants are all one of a kind, a situation that developed when the "turnkey" approach was abandoned early in the commercialization process. Nevertheless, progress in standardization is being made. Standard U.S. reactor plant designs are now undergoing the NRC certification process.

Public Perception

Public opinion about nuclear power and its role in our energy future is important to further nuclear development. Over the years, public opinion polls have reflected a variety of attitudes, but public awareness of the need for energy planning for the future has increased. Partly as a result of worldwide concern over the greenhouse effect, recent polls suggest that a majority of people expect nuclear power to play an increased role in electricity supply. On the other hand, studies

Public opinion about nuclear power and its role in our energy future is important to further nuclear development.

have consistently shown that the general public considers nuclear hazards to be greater than shown by technical evaluations such as probabilistic risk assessment.

The reasons for public opinion at any given time are the subject of debate, and often there may be more than one valid reason. Very early in the development of nuclear power, any concern of its potential hazards seemed to be overridden by fascination with the promise of peaceful applications. But as

Nuclear power protest in Washington, DC. (Courtesy of U.S. Council for Energy Awareness)

nuclear power expanded rapidly in the 1960s, many people suddenly were faced with making their own assessment of personal risk, without a good basis for doing so.

This first spurt of growth coincided with increased public disillusionment with big institutions. A substantial number of people felt that large institutions, both public and private, should share some of the blame for the ills of society. The nuclear industry, with its genesis in the Manhattan Project and its business conducted in the regulatory spotlight, stood out as a major institution. It has been suggested that it was this distrust of institutions that formed the basis for the first public disaffection with nuclear energy.[14]

The first major commercial reactor accident occurred at a time when an appreciable sector of the public already had some concern over the safety of nuclear reactors. The physical consequences of the accident at TMI-2 were limited to the reactor plant itself. The losses were financial; neither the workers nor the neighboring population were hurt. In fact, the term "meltdown" was gradually replaced with "core damage" in the nuclear lexicon, because exami-

---

[14]Llewellyn King, "Understanding the Press: The Publisher's Perspective," *The Energy Daily* (Feb. 5, 1990).

nation of TMI showed that rubble in the substantial section of core destroyed by the accident looked nothing like the molten mass portrayed by oversimplified severe accident analyses. The entire core was contained within the reactor vessel, the third physical barrier to radioactive materials. But the combination of confusion, lack of experience with such events, and the resultant fear led to a week of significant public trauma, followed by a lingering uneasiness with nuclear power. In the United States, the impact of the TMI-2 accident on public confidence was severe.

> Chernobyl notwithstanding, nuclear power remains one of the safest and most environmentally benign forms of energy generation.

Utilities were hit by the cost penalties involved in conservatively adapting all of the lessons learned from TMI to plants already built and under construction. The Department of Energy estimated that the required "backfits" cost an average of 65 million dollars per operating reactor. Escalation of capital costs for new plants because of high interest rates, regulatory delays, and other factors had already taken some of the bloom off the utilities' romance with nuclear power. Rising costs, coupled with the dramatic reduction in demand for electrical generating capacity following the surprise increases in oil prices in 1973 and 1976, caused many utilities to defer or cancel nuclear plant orders.

The impact of TMI was felt mainly in the United States. Although orders for new nuclear plants also fell off in much of the Western world, this was primarily due to changing economic conditions.[15] European heads of states reaffirmed their belief in nuclear power in 1979. Nuclear development sustained momentum in much of the industrial world until Chernobyl.

Chernobyl is simply impossible to discuss within the framework of Western design and operating standards. Analyses have shown that if the reactor had just had a containment building of the type that all U.S. reactors have, no radioactivity would have escaped, and the world probably would never have heard of Chernobyl.[16] But there was no effective containment, and the catastrophe led to a worldwide public backlash against nuclear power. The impact was felt across international borders; extolling the safety of Western reactors could not assure all sectors of a skeptical and sometimes angry public.

Chernobyl notwithstanding, nuclear power remains one of the safest and most environmentally benign forms of energy generation. Considering that

---

[15]Bertrand Goldschmidt, *The Atomic Complex*, American Nuclear Society, La Grange Park, IL (1982).
[16]Bernard Cohen, *The Nuclear Energy Option*, Plenum Press (1990).

more than 400 nuclear power plants have been deployed around the world within the past 25 years, the safety record for this completely new technology has been exemplary. Today's PWRs and BWRs have robust designs and conservative operating conditions that defend the principal nuclear safety objective—to protect individuals, society, and the environment from radiological hazards. TMI-2 and Chernobyl both sustained severe core damage, but Chernobyl released over one million times more radioactive material than TMI-2. Successful application of the defense-in-depth philosophy protected the Pennsylvania community.

Nevertheless, the cost of the TMI-2 accident exceeded one billion dollars. It was a dramatic demonstration that owners of nuclear power plants have strong financial incentive to operate their plants safely, stopping potential accidents before the second physical barrier can be breached. Poorly operated plants also waste money because of inefficiency and regulatory intervention. Nuclear plant operators have demonstrated their desire to improve operations through the formation of self-regulation organizations aimed at bringing every plant up to high operating standards.

Despite the good safety record of current LWRs, there are a significant number of people who believe that reactors should be even more forgiving of operator errors and external events. It is felt that the resultant reduction in the probability of core damage would boost the confidence of utility investors and a skeptical public. Next-generation nuclear plants are being designed with this in mind. Japan has already committed to construct an advanced BWR before the end of the century.

BIBLIOGRAPHY

————. 1988. *Basic Safety Principles for Nuclear Power Plants.* International Atomic Energy Agency.

————. 1962 and supplement 1967. *Civilian Nuclear Power: A Report to the President.* U.S. Atomic Energy Commission.

Cohen, Bernard. 1990. *The Nuclear Energy Option.* Plenum Press.

Crane, Landon T. 1980. "Coal and Nuclear Power Policies: Seeking Protection from Uncertain Risks; A Review of Health, Safety and Environmental Factors," Congressional Research Service Report No. 80/40 SPR.

Edelson, Edward. 1988. *The Journalist's Guide to Nuclear Energy.* U.S. Council for Energy Awareness.

Goldschmidt, Bertrand. 1982. *The Atomic Complex.* American Nuclear Society, La Grange Park, IL.

King, Llewellyn. Feb. 5, 1990. "Understanding the Press: The Publisher's Perspective." *The Energy Daily.*

Lapp, Ralph. 1974. *The Nuclear Controversy.* Fact Systems.

Leclercq, Jacques. 1986. *The Nuclear Age.* Sodel.

Lederer, Edith M., and Sergel Shargorodsky. July 1992. "The Soviet Nuclear Legacy." Associated Press Report.

Medvedev, Grigoriy. June 1989. "Chernobyl Notebook," *Novy Mir*.

————. 1991. "National Energy Strategy—Powerful Ideas for America," 1st ed. U.S. Department of Energy.

Pocock, R. F. 1977. *Nuclear Power, Its Development in the United Kingdom*. The Institution of Nuclear Engineers.

————. 1955. *Proceedings of the International Conference on Peaceful Uses of Atomic Energy*. United Nations.

————. 1975. "Reactor Safety Study—An Assessment of Accident Risks in U.S. Commercial Nuclear Power Plants," WASH-1400. U.S. Nuclear Regulatory Commission.

Shihab-Eldin, Adnan, Alexander Shlyakhter, and Richard Wilson, "Is There a Large Risk of Radiation? A Critical Review of Pessimistic Claims," ANL-92/23. Argonne National Laboratory (1992).

————. 1957. "Theoretical Possibilities and Consequences of Major Accidents in Large Nuclear Power Plants," WASH-740. U.S. Atomic Energy Commission.

Uranium recovered from pyrochemical processing in the Integral Fast Reactor technology development program. (Courtesy of Argonne National Laboratory)

EIGHT

Working Toward a Nuclear Future

The research, development, and commercialization activities going on today can provide a glimpse of the possible future for applications of nuclear energy. Of course, the bright future promised by technical achievements could be clouded by nontechnical developments in politics and public perception. The intent here is to provide a brief description only of the potential promise offered by some of the technical programs, without consideration of the role of institutional issues.

Nuclear Science and Technology

Nuclear medicine is assured of continuing to be an exciting growth area in the health care industry. For many diagnostic tests, there are simply no effective alternatives to nuclear medical techniques. Because medical treatment and research with labeled compounds rely on substitution of a radioactive isotope for a stable isotope with identical chemical properties, nuclear medicine is also becoming known as "molecular medicine." Labeled compounds are being used to pinpoint the extent of infections, particularly important if surgery is to be performed. Major advances will continue with research using radiotracers to study the metabolic pathways of new drugs and the functioning of body systems, because no competing techniques exist for noninvasive study of such processes in either healthy or diseased organs. Some nuclear medical techniques, such as positron emission tomography (PET) scans, may be too expensive for widespread application, but will be used at research centers to develop a better understanding of the functioning of specific organs.

For cancer treatment, a variety of ongoing experimental testing promises new nuclear techniques. Research is centered around developing techniques to deliver higher doses directly to a malignant tumor without excessive damage to healthy tissue. One technique being tried is the insertion of a radioactive implant directly into the tumor; the implant is removed once the tumor is destroyed. Research also continues with labeled monoclonal antibodies, with present emphasis aimed at finding ways to attach alpha emitters to tumors. Alpha particles can deliver more energy in a much shorter range than beta emitters, a single "hit" causing significant destruction within a cell. Bismuth-212, astatine-211, and fermium-252 are being used as alpha emitters in experiments with monoclonal antibodies.

A third type of treatment technique that will be tested in the 1990s is called *boron neutron capture therapy* (BNCT). In this technique, a nuclear reactor is used directly to treat a malignant tumor. BNCT requires selective assimilation of a benign boron drug by the tumor. The surface of the body in the region of the tumor is irradiated with low-energy neutrons. Boron-10, present primarily in the tumor, has a high neutron capture cross section and absorbs a significant fraction of the neutrons in the beam. When B-10 captures a neutron, it splits into two massive charged particles, an alpha particle and a lithium nucleus. Because of their size and electric charge, these particles lose their 2400 keV of energy in a short range compared to that of the beta particles used in other nuclear therapy procedures. Typically, this energy may be completely deposited within a single cell, resulting in significant destruction in the cell. Although the boron drug may also be deposited in such remote organs as the kidneys and the liver, they suffer no unnecessary damage because the neutron beam is localized in the tumor region. In the United States, experiments thus far have been limited to brain tumors in dogs. However, in Japan there has been some successful treatment of humans suffering from glioblastoma multiforme—the most deadly type of brain tumor, for which there is no other viable treatment.

Neutron scattering experiments are finding ever broader applications. For example, research and development of high-temperature superconductors is a major initiative that relies on neutron scattering to determine some properties of superconducting materials. The next decade will see the development of new facilities and enhancement of capabilities at existing facilities. In the United States, construction of a new materials research reactor called the Advanced Neutron Source is planned at Oak Ridge National Laboratory. The new reactor has been designed to have at least a factor of 5 higher neutron flux than the most powerful existing facilities. Initial planning for improved pulsed source capabilities is also under way in Europe and the United States, with the goal of order-of-magnitude improvement in source strength. Development of improved instruments and neutron moderators such as solid methane are ongoing activities.

The recent use of neutron radiography for inspection of airplanes for structural corrosion has been successful. Previously, complete disassembly was required for inspection. Neutron radiography has cut in half the time and effort required to make this type of repair, making expansion of this capability with the addition of new facilities seem to be a logical next step. If current efforts to demonstrate an effective explosives detector are successful, there could be a rapid expansion of neutron radiography techniques into the transportation security market.

Space nuclear power sources will continue to be used for applications for which they are the only viable option. United Nations agreements may limit some applications, but the safety principles under consideration are generally acceptable to nations involved in space applications, research, and exploration. Work on the development of suitable reactor power sources for space is ongoing in the United States, including consideration of adapting the successful Russian Topaz reactor. Nuclear propulsion, in which interest has been rekindled as a result of the recent U.S. Space Exploration Initiative, appears to be an enabling technology for a number of missions involving both manned and unmanned transport to the near planets.

Fusion

All of today's nuclear power plants are based on the fission process, in which a neutron is absorbed by a uranium or transuranic nucleus, causing it to split into two energetic fragments and several free neutrons. Future nuclear power plants may have the option of using fusion,[1] the process that powers the sun and other stars. Fusion releases energy when two light nuclei collide to form a single heavier nucleus and emit an energetic neutron or proton.

For more than 40 years, researchers around the world have been conducting experiments trying to harness fusion with the goal of developing a central power station. Most fusion research today is focused on experimental devices called *tokamaks*, which were conceived in the early 1950s by the Russian physicists Andrei Sakharov and Igor Tamm. Tokamaks use very strong magnetic fields to confine a doughnut-shaped plasma (an ionized gas) in a toroidal vacuum chamber. Another branch of fusion research uses very high power lasers or particle beams to compress small pellets of fuel until the nuclei fuse, in essentially the same way that the fuel in a hydrogen bomb is compressed until it fuses.

At least the first generation of fusion reactors will fuse deuterium, a heavy rare isotope of hydrogen available in any ordinary water, and tritium, a still heavier and radioactive isotope of hydrogen produced by neutron irradiation of lithium. Later generations would use only deuterium. The helium produced in the deuterium-tritium fusion process is not itself radioactive, but the neutrons, which carry 75% of the energy, cause the structures and coolant of the reactor to become radioactive. Because some materials become more radioactive than others, the proper choice of materials is an important step in achieving the safety potential of fusion power.

---

[1]This section is drawn extensively from Robert W. Conn, Valery A. Chuyanov, Nobuyuki Inoe, and Donald R. Sweetman, "The International Thermonuclear Experimental Reactors," *Scientific American*, pp. 102–110 (April 1992).

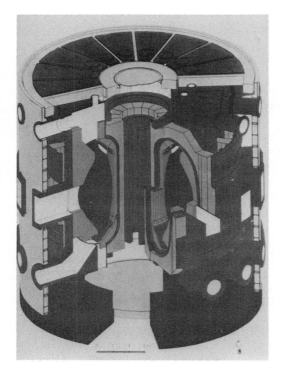

Artist's conception of the International Thermonuclear Experimental Reactor, which is to demonstrate the feasibility of magnetic fusion power. (Courtesy of U.S. Department of Energy)

The motivation for developing a fusion reactor is simple—the promise of an almost limitless nuclear fuel supply that would produce less radioactive waste when consumed. However, achieving that promise in an economic fusion plant will be a daunting scientific and engineering task. A significant milestone in that quest was achieved in November 1991 at the Joint European Torus (JET) facility at Culham Laboratory in the United Kingdom. Researchers observed an energy pulse of approximately 1 MW of thermal power for two seconds (several percent of the power required to drive the test) in a controlled experiment using only 0.2 grams of tritium in a deuterium plasma.

The scientific and engineering challenges of developing fusion power have led the four major fusion research groups to combine their talents for the design and construction of a single device. The International Thermonuclear Experimental Reactor (ITER) is a collaborative effort by the United States, the European Community, Japan, and Russia to design and build a tokamak producing 1000 MW of thermal power. The conceptual design of the experimental reactor took place during 1988–1990 in Garching, Germany, with workers from all the participating countries involved. The engineering design begins in 1992 with work being done in Germany, the United States, and Japan, with oversight by the ITER Council in Moscow. The site of the ITER experiment itself has not yet been determined. Construction of the facility is scheduled to be completed by 2004, with commissioning in 2005 at a total estimated cost of $7.5 billion.

ITER will be the largest tokamak ever built, about 25 meters in diameter and 30 meters high. The plasma chamber will measure 4.2×8.4 meters and may be lined with carbon-fiber composite tiles mounted on water-cooled pipes. Initially, ITER will not produce its own tritium. Rather, the blanket surrounding the plasma will simply absorb the neutrons released in the fusion reactions. Later, tritium will be produced by placing a lithium compound in stainless steel tubes or boxes in the blanket. The superconducting magnets surrounding the chamber will produce a peak magnetic field of approximately 4.85 tesla, which is about 100,000 times stronger than the earth's magnetic field. If ITER is successful, fusion power could start to contribute to the global energy supply by the middle of the next century.

Nuclear Power Production

There is no question that the production of electricity by nuclear power faces difficulties and uncertainties in many of the 32 nations producing nuclear electricity today. Difficulties are highlighted by public concerns about the ultimate disposal of nuclear waste and a public perception that underestimates the relative safety of nuclear power generation. In several countries, uncertainties about the stability of the regulatory environment and the lifetime costs of new plants are partially responsible for postponing investment in new nuclear generating stations. Many nations have programs in place to address these issues. But the plain facts are that western nuclear power plants are exceptionally safe, the former Soviet plants are being brought up to higher safety standards, and all nuclear plants are nonpolluting. The volume of nuclear waste generated is very small for the amount of power generated, and current national initiatives will find acceptable solutions both to the backlog and future wastes. Further, electricity growth has been inexorably linked to economic growth, and nuclear power is the only technology that can be counted on to accommodate increasing electrical demand through the next century.

The environmental and human-health problems of fossil fuels will discourage widespread expansion of coal use, although increased use of cleaner burning natural gas is expected. Oil will still be needed in the transportation market, although there is a big push to develop electric vehicles for urban commuting—only adding to future electrical demands. Conservation should relieve some of the need for new electrical generating capacity, but there are practical and economic limits to what can be done. Also, there are older plants of all types that must be replaced in the decades ahead. The largest demand for new electrical capacity may come from third world countries, as they strive for equity with their more affluent neighbors. Renewable resources are expected to provide a share of the new capacity, but this unproven approach cannot be expected to fill much of the gap between the needs of the twenty-first century and what today's production and improved conservation can provide. The question may not be whether nuclear will provide any of the new capacity needed for worldwide economic growth, but whether the nuclear component can be expanded rapidly enough to meet the demand for environmentally acceptable electrical power.

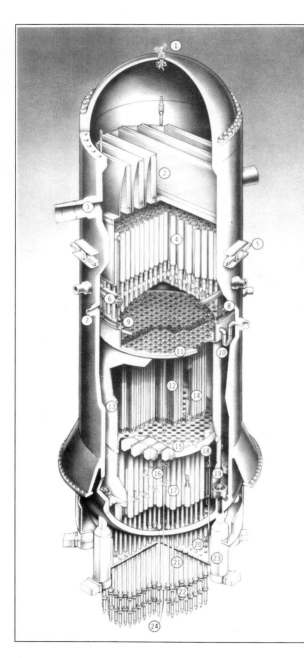

Advanced Boiling Water Reactor Assembly

1   Vent and Head Spray
2   Steam Dryer
3   Steam Outlet Flow Restrictor
4   Steam Separators
5   RPV Stabilizer
6   Feedwater Sparger
7   Shutdown Cooling Outlet
8   Low Pressure Flooder (LPFL)
    and Shutdown Cooling Sparger
9   High Pressure Core Flooder
    (HPCF) Sparger
10 HPCF Coupling
11 Top Guide
12 Fuel Assemblies
13 Core Shroud
14 Control Rod
15 Core Plate
16 In-Core Instrument Guide
    Tubes
17 Control Rod Guide Tubes
18 Core Differential Pressure Line
19 Reactor Internal Pumps (RIP)
20 Thermal Insulation
21 Control Rod Drive Housings
22 Fine Motion Control Rod
    Drives
23 RIP Motor Casing
24 Local Power Range Monitor

GE Nuclear Energy

General Electric's ABWR. (Courtesy of General Electric)

Governments and industries are preparing for future expansion of nuclear power. In the intermediate term, water-cooled reactors will continue to dominate the nuclear power technologies deployed. A number of evolution-ary improvements to LWRs are being pursued for present and soon-to-come plant designs. More revolutionary changes to LWRs are also being proposed, but these plants will not be deployed for several years at least. Work on the high-temperature gas-cooled reactor (HTGR) continues, primarily in the United States, while the further development of heavy water reactors is primarily a Canadian undertaking. In the longer term, a few decades away perhaps, fast breeder reactors under development in several nations should begin to take over from LWRs to extend the lifetime of nuclear fission-generated electricity indefinitely.

In the Commonwealth of Independent States (CIS), nuclear development plans are on hold while the political and economic adjustments are being made. One international activity is an evaluation of existing nuclear power plants in the CIS relative to western safety standards. Important improve-ments in operating procedures have been made. Some technical changes have been made, while others are being prioritized as funding is being sought. Ironically, newer, safer VVER plants under construction have been put on hold, while older RMBR plants have been kept running to provide needed electricity.

Advanced Light Water Reactors

The nuclear energy industry is working aggressively to develop advanced nuclear energy plants for the 1990s and beyond. In the United States,[2] the U.S. Department of Energy (DOE), the nuclear utilities through the Electric Power Research Institute (EPRI), and the major reactor manufacturers and architect-engineering firms are directing design efforts on a number of advanced approaches, two of which are successors to the current light water technolo-gies: the large [900- to 1300-MW(e)] evolutionary advanced light water cooled reactors (ALWRs), including the *advanced boiling water reactor* (ABWR) and the *advanced pressurized water reactor* (APWR); and the midsized [600-MW(e)] passive ALWRs, including the *simplified boiling water reactor* (SBWR) and the *advanced pressurized reactor* (AP600). These two types of advanced designs should receive U.S. Nuclear Regulatory Commission (NRC) design certifica-tion during the 1990s.

In addition, other reactor designs are being developed by domestic and international companies: The *safe integral reactor* (SIR), the *pressurized heavy water reactor* (CANDU 3), and the *process inherent ultimate safety reactor* (PIUS). The companies developing the reactors also seek NRC design certification.

---

[2]This description of advanced LWRs is based on materials supplied by the U.S. Council on Energy Awareness.

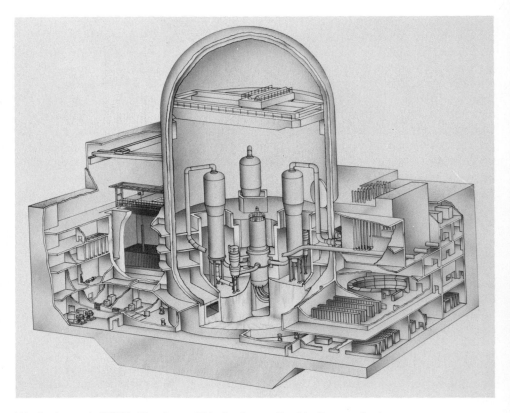

Westinghouse's APWR. (Courtesy of Westinghouse Electric Corporation)

While the advanced reactor types differ, the designs have been developed with several common goals: a simpler design, economy and predictability in all costs (capital, operation, maintenance, and fuel), less reliance on complex engineered systems and reduced need for rapid operator actions to assure safety, and assured licensability and standardization.

The current trend in France, the United Kingdom, Germany, and other European nations is to retain many of the features of existing PWRs, while improving some parts of the plant. The concerns in Europe are somewhat different from those in the United States, leading to somewhat new design requirements for next-generation PWRs. For example, the operation of large-scale European reprocessing plants opens the door for using recycled mixed plutonium-uranium oxide (MOX) fuel in LWRs, which in the past has been done only on a small scale.

In the United Kingdom, where nuclear power sources in 1991 accounted for 19.5% of the total electricity production, the Magnox and advanced gas-cooled

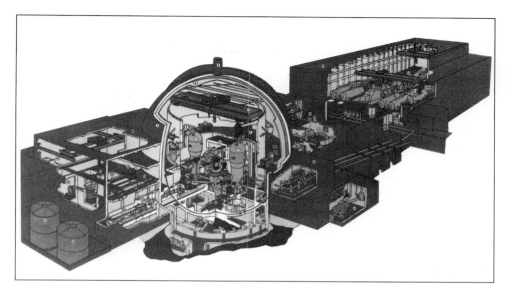

ABB Combustion Engineering's System 80+. (Courtesy of ABB Combustion Engineering)

reactors now in service will continue a dominant role for the near future. Construction of the Sizewell B PWR station, the United Kingdom's first PWR, continues to run ahead of schedule and within cost estimates. In spite of continued good experience with its gas-cooled reactors, the common expectation is that future U.K. nuclear plants will be PWRs.

In France, where more than 70% of the electricity is produced by nuclear power, a new generation of PWRs is being developed in cooperation with other European countries. France has developed an evolutionary PWR called the N4 that Framatome is installing in three units under construction in France. These 1455-MW(e) plants will be the world's largest LWRs. Another major development is French and German industry cooperation on the Nuclear Power International (NPI) project, with the aim of designing a joint French-German PWR. The target construction date for this first-of-a-kind plant is 1998.

In Asia, Japan and the Republic of Korea are participating with other countries in developing and demonstrating advanced LWR technologies. Asea Brown Boveria/Combustion Engineering's (ABB/C-E's) large ALWR, System 80+, has been designed with the help of the Korea Advanced Energy Research Institute. Korea has two System 80 plants, a precursor to System 80+, under construction.

Japan, which has essentially no indigenous fossil fuel resources, has an active nuclear development program. The two large ABWRs, 1350-MW(e) plants, are being built for the Tokyo Electric Power Company, as a cooperative

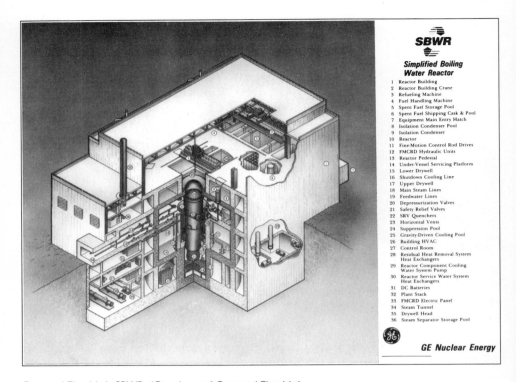

SBWR

Simplified Boiling Water Reactor

1 Reactor Building
2 Reactor Building Crane
3 Refueling Machine
4 Fuel Handling Machine
5 Spent Fuel Storage Pool
6 Spent Fuel Shipping Cask & Pool
7 Equipment Main Entry Hatch
8 Isolation Condenser Pool
9 Isolation Condenser
10 Reactor
11 Fine-Motion Control Rod Drives
12 FMCRD Hydraulic Units
13 Reactor Pedestal
14 Under-Vessel Servicing Platform
15 Lower Drywell
16 Shutdown Cooling Line
17 Upper Drywell
18 Main Steam Lines
19 Feedwater Lines
20 Depressurization Valves
21 Safety Relief Valves
22 SRV Quenchers
23 Horizontal Vents
24 Suppression Pool
25 Gravity-Driven Cooling Pool
26 Building HVAC
27 Control Room
28 Residual Heat Removal System Heat Exchangers
29 Reactor Component Cooling Water System Pump
30 Reactor Service Water System Heat Exchangers
31 DC Batteries
32 Plant Stack
33 FMCRD Electric Panel
34 Steam Tunnel
35 Drywell Head
36 Steam Separator Storage Pool

GE Nuclear Energy

General Electric's SBWR. (Courtesy of General Electric)

venture between GE, Hitachi Ltd., and Toshiba Corporation. Hitachi and Toshiba have been partners with GE in commercializing BWR technology in Japan. Similarly, Mitsubishi Heavy Industries, Ltd., has been a partner with Westinghouse in commercializing the PWR in Japan. Japanese utilities are planning to build an APWR plant as the next PWR project. One goal Japan has for longer term LWR development is burning of MOX fuel, which will be produced domestically as well as imported from Europe.

The Large ALWRs. These 900- to 1300-MW(e) reactors are advanced versions of current light water reactors with significant, evolutionary improvements. Lessons learned from the currently operating plants have been factored into the design of the evolutionary ALWRs along with several new improvements over previous LWR technology. The Westinghouse APWR 1300 earned its Preliminary Design Authorization from the U.S. NRC in 1991. Westinghouse has also designed a 1000-MW(e) version of the APWR, primarily for overseas sales. NRC design certifications for General Electric's ABWR and ABB/C-E's System 80+ PWR design are expected in the early to mid-1990s.

Westinghouse's AP-600. (Courtesy of Westinghouse Electric Corporation)

The Midsized Passive ALWRs.   These 600-MW(e) designs include General Electric's simplified boiling water reactor and Westinghouse's advanced passive pressurized water reactor (AP-600). Two differences between these passive designs and the evolutionary light water reactors are the smaller size and the added passive safety features that no longer rely on on-site support systems. These "passive" systems take advantage of natural forces (gravity, for example) rather than powered machinery, moving parts, or operator action to prevent accidents that could result from upset conditions. NRC is expected to certify these designs in the mid-1990s.

The Safe Integral Reactor.   ABB/C-E, Stone and Webster, Rolls-Royce, and the United Kingdom Atomic Energy Authority have completed the conceptual design for a 320-MW(e) light water reactor with passive safety features. All of the conventional primary loop components (reactor, pumps,

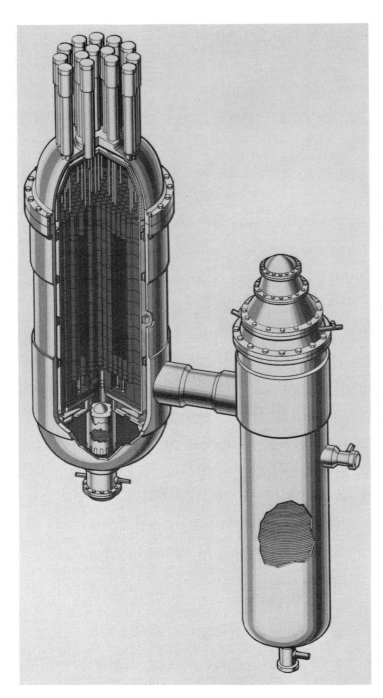

MHTGR nuclear
steam supply system.
(Courtesy of General
Atomics)

steam generator, and pressurizer) are integrated into a single vessel, thereby eliminating all large coolant pipes.

The Process Inherent Ultimate Safety Reactor.   The ABB/C-E's PIUS 600-MW(e) reactor is essentially a reactor entirely surrounded with borated water and placed in a prestressed concrete vessel. The design offers passive mechanisms for cooling and shutdown of the reactor during accident conditions without any need for immediate operator intervention. This design will require a prototype demonstration before it can be certified.

The Advanced Heavy Water Reactor.   The CANDU 3, with a net electrical output of 450 MW, is an evolutionary version of the CANDU advanced heavy water energy plants offered by Atomic Energy of Canada, Ltd. The plant will be fully modularized. All key components (steam generators, coolant pumps, pressure tubes, etc.) will be identical to those proven in service in operating CANDU energy stations. The design would most likely be demonstrated in Canada before introduction into the United States.

High-Temperature Gas-Cooled Reactors

Gas-cooled reactor development in much of the world has been terminated in favor of advanced LWR development. However, in the United States, General Atomics, with support from the U.S. Department of Energy, has been developing a concept called the *modular high-temperature gas-cooled reactor* (MHTGR).[3] Its features are typical of an HTGR—inert helium gas coolant, graphite moderator and core structural material, and refractory-coated particle fuel. The design for the MHTGR is based on the earlier HTGRs, including Peach Bottom 1 and Fort St. Vrain in the United States and more than 50 gas-cooled reactors in the United Kingdom, France, Germany, and Japan.

A commercial MHTGR facility would consist of four reactor modules coupled to two steam turbine generators. Each module is currently designed to provide approximately 140 MW(e). The design outlet temperature of the helium from the core is 687°C, which enables the system's thermal efficiency (approximately 40%) to exceed that of a conventional light water reactor. General Atomics is hoping to create a market niche based on modular construction, improved thermal efficiency, and improved natural resistance to accidents.

The MHTGR takes advantage of the inherent features of the system to yield a design that is said to depend neither on active engineered safety features nor human actions for protection against severe low-probability accidents. Some of the inherent features of the system are (1) an inert coolant, (2) a graphite core

---

[3] *The Modular High Temperature Gas-Cooled Reactor: Inherently Safe Nuclear Power*, General Atomics.

that is stable at high temperatures and provides a large heat sink, (3) coated fuel particles that retain fission products up to very high temperatures, (4) a reactor size that allows for decay heat removal by passive means (convective and radiative cooling), (5) below-ground installation, which aids in cooling and provides an additional barrier (along with the reactor vessel) against air/oxygen reactions with graphite, and (6) a strong negative temperature coefficient and a zero coolant void coefficient that cause the reactor to shut down automatically should the temperature rise abnormally.

The design requires a prototype demonstration plant. MHTGRs could be commercially available in the next decade.

Sodium-Cooled Fast Breeder Reactors

Sodium-cooled fast breeder reactors have been viewed since the earliest days of reactor development as the ultimate nuclear power systems because of their unique ability to use all of the uranium resource. This resource extension is of critical importance to the magnitude and duration of the contribution that nuclear plants can make to electricity supply. Estimates of the uranium resources that are economically recoverable in the world outside the centrally planned economies and the former Soviet Union are published annually by the Organization for Economic Cooperation and Development (OECD). In 1988, the estimate was 3.6 million tonnes of uranium. In the sector of the world within the OECD purview, current nuclear plant capacity is about 290,000 MW(e), essentially all of it thermal reactors. If operated in the simplest mode (once-through, i.e., no reprocessing) this capacity would require about 50,000 tonnes of uranium per year. The stated OECD estimate of recoverable resources would then be depleted in about 70 years. If instead, because of environmental, economic, energy security, or other reasons, LWRs or other thermal reactor deployment were increased significantly, the uranium would be exhausted proportionally sooner. By contrast, if breeders were the dominant reactors deployed and they utilized all the uranium resources, a few thousand 1000-MW(e) plants could be fueled for several thousand years.

The resource depletion issue is not pressing today, but it is equally clear that only with breeder reactors can nuclear fission plants provide a large long-term electrical generation source. On the other hand, need for the breeder, if based on resource depletion, which is at least a few decades in the future, is probably not a sufficient reason by itself to sustain the relatively large development programs still necessary to bring these reactors to commercialization. Breeders must be able to compete in the relative near term on the basis of their economics, their safety, and perhaps other characteristics. Today this is the thrust of all breeder reactor development programs worldwide.

Breeder technology was among the first to be tested in the AEC's reactor development program. EBR-I generated the first electricity from nuclear

Phénix, the 230-MW(e) LMFBR at Marcoule in France. (Courtesy of Electricité de France)

fission in 1951. EBR-I was followed by EBR-II, which achieved first criticality in 1964. EBR-II was built to demonstrate all the elements of sodium-cooled reactors at prototype scale, including electricity generation of 19 MW(e). It did this superbly, not only operating to this day, but it is now once again the nucleus of the U.S. advanced reactor development program.

Breeder development programs began early in several other countries. In the United Kingdom, the major milestones included the Dounreay Fast Reactor (DFR), which at 14 MW(e) operated from 1959–1977. It was followed by the Prototype Fast Reactor (PFR), which generates 250 MW(e), began operation in 1974, and continues operation to the present.

Creys-Malville, Super Phénix, which is a 1200-MW(e) LMFBR in Bouvesse, France. (Courtesy of Electricité de France)

France emerged as the leader in the effort to commercialize this technology with Rhapsodie in 1967, followed by the 230-MW(e) Phénix plant in 1973, which is still operating today. France also has built the largest breeder plant to date, the 1200-MW(e) Super Phénix, which achieved first criticality on September 7, 1985. Japan also has an active breeder development program, and will be the most recent nation to join those with demonstration plants when the 280-MW(e) Monju plant is completed next year. A predecessor to Monju, the Joyo plant began operation in 1977 and continues operating currently.

Today, no new firmly planned breeder plant projects are on the drawing boards. All development programs are attempting to define a next step with improved economics and enhanced safety as major objectives.

In Europe, the French, British, and German programs are cooperating on the European Fast Reactor (EFR) development. The EFR project is approaching the end of phase 2, which consists of concept validation. By the middle of 1993, the

Interior of Monju, a 280-MW(e) LMFBR under construction at Tsuruga, Japan. (Courtesy of Power Reactor and Nuclear Fuel Development Corporation)

main options will have been confirmed and a consistent preliminary design will be available, including a cost estimate of a prototype. The aim of the EFR project is a large fast reactor plant, still safer and less expensive than those now operating. After completion of phase 2, it will be up to the governments and utilities to determine the next step.

In Japan, studies are being conducted on a demonstration fast breeder reactor to follow Monju. This plant is currently planned to be commissioned shortly after the year 2000.

Sodium-cooled reactor programs in Europe and Japan today remain centered on traditional lines of breeder development: ceramic fuel in the form of uranium-plutonium oxide, and a closed fuel cycle (which breeders require in one form or another to use the resources completely) based on the aqueous Purex reprocessing technology.

In the United States, breeder development has taken a quite different turn, given the particular circumstances of the U.S. program. With the cancellation in 1983 of the Clinch River Breeder Reactor (CRBR)—the U.S. demonstration plant equivalent to Phénix, PFR, or Monju—the U.S. program had to take a new approach. There would be no U.S. demonstration plant for a long time, which enabled researchers to take a new look at fundamental features of the breeder. Even before CRBR cancellation, it became clear that there would be no U.S. Purex reprocessing capabilities upon which to build the traditional fast reactor oxide fuel cycle. The U.S. line of development has been based increasingly since 1984 on the Integral Fast Reactor (IFR). Rather than uranium oxide, the fuel is a uranium-plutonium-zirconium metal alloy, an outgrowth of many years of successful experience with metal fuel in EBR-II. Metal fuel raises the possibility of a much different fuel cycle technology called the *pyroprocess*. The pyroprocess appears to be a simple and compact technology that may be economically deployable in small sizes, perhaps in sizes that serve only one or a few reactor plants. If so, the fuel cycle plants could be deployed with very few reactors only as needed. The pyroprocess will soon be tested in the United States by Argonne National Laboratory.

General Electric Company has adopted the features of the IFR in a commercial design concept called the *power reactor innovative small module* (PRISM). GE is proposing construction of a single module as a demonstration of its features. The NRC will require a prototype demonstration for IFR technology.

Developing enhanced safety characteristics is a goal of every breeder reactor development program. With sodium as a coolant, one unique safety characteristic is that the coolant operates at temperatures far below boiling, and the reactor core and primary coolant system can operate at very low pressure. Depressurization accidents are of no concern. While sodium reacts in air and reacts strongly in water and therefore must be isolated, experience worldwide with the handling and isolation of sodium has been excellent.

As a demonstration of possible safety characteristics in sodium-cooled reactors, the 1986 tests in EBR-II are a landmark series. From full power, with normal automatic reactor shutdown systems deliberately bypassed, power was cut off to the sodium coolant pumps, and the very unlikely loss-of-flow (without automatic shutdown) accident was simulated. Because of its sodium coolant and metal fuel, EBR-II simply shut itself off from the full-power condition without operator action or action by any active safety system. While the details may vary, this sort of passive safety response is the goal of all sodium-cooled reactor development programs.

Sodium-cooled reactors are now gaining increased attention for two other potentially exciting reasons—reducing the risk from nuclear weapons that will be dismantled as the Cold War draws to an end, and reducing by a large factor the duration of the radiological hazard of nuclear waste placed in permanent storage. When a transuranic element (e.g., plutonium, neptunium, americium, or curium) captures a neutron, it can fission to produce energy or it can simply retain the neutron and transmute to the next isotope up the chain (for example, a neutron captured by Pu-239 results in Pu-240). The basic neutron physics of sodium-cooled fast reactors is such that, relative to today's reactors, they maximize fission relative to transmutation. Stated more simply, transuranic elements are simply fuel for a fast reactor, whereas thermal reactors tend to build up more and higher isotopes. This property of preferentially fissioning the transuranic elements is needed if they are to be eliminated while producing beneficial energy. Weapons plutonium could be readily blended with other materials and cast into fuel pins for use in LMRs. Properly used or stored, the fuel would greatly reduce the potential for misusing the plutonium to assemble another weapon. Similarly, with reprocessing and use as LMR fuel, the transuranic elements could be eliminated from high-level nuclear waste, reducing the storage requirement from more than ten thousand years to only a few hundred years.

In the 50 years since CP-1 and the 40+ years since EBR-I, sodium-cooled breeder reactors have come a long way. It will be many years, however, before they can be deployed in significant numbers. Meanwhile, research and development continue in several countries with increasing international cooperation.

These programs are all focused on improving the economics of the technology, capitalizing on the unique safety features of sodium-cooled plants, and developing a range of fuel cycle options including perhaps the ability to recycle and consume many of the long-lived waste elements. Above all, though, the greatest promise of the sodium-cooled breeder remains unchanged—the ability to provide essentially limitless electrical energy from nuclear fission.

BIBLIOGRAPHY

————. August 1992. "Boston Attendees Examine the Value of the Atom," *Nucl. News.*

Conn, Robert W., Valery A. Chuyanov, Nobuyuki Inoe, and Donald R. Sweetman. April 1992. "The International Thermonuclear Experimental Reactor," *Sci. Am.,* pp. 102–110.

Golay, M. W., and N. E. Todreas. April 1990. "Advanced Light-Water Reactors," *Sci. Am.*

————. *The Modular High Temperature Gas-Cooled Reactor: Inherently Safe Nuclear Power.* General Atomics.

Smith, D. J. March 1990. "Nuclear Suppliers Prepare for the Next Generation of Orders," *Power Eng.*

Till, C. E., and Y. I. Chang. 1989. "Evolution of the Liquid Metal Reactor: The Integral Fast Reactor (IFR) Concept," in *Proceedings of the American Power Conference.*

————. August 1992. "World List of Nuclear Power Plants," *Nucl. News.*